REVISE C2

for MEI Structured Mathematics

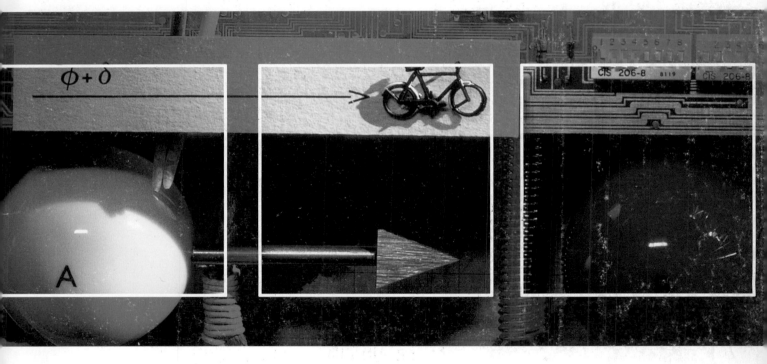

Series Editor
Roger Porkess

Authors
Catherine Berry, Diana Boynova, Tom Button,
Diana Cowey and Sue de Pomerai

HODDER
EDUCATION
AN HACHETTE UK COMPANY

Every effort has been made to trace all copyright holders, but if any have been inadvertently overlooked the Publishers will be pleased to make the necessary arrangements at the first opportunity.

Although every effort has been made to ensure that website addresses are correct at time of going to press, Hodder Education cannot be held responsib e for the content of any website mentioned in this book. It is sometimes possible to find a relocated web page by typing in the address of the home page for a website in the URL window of your browser.

Hachette Livre UK's policy is to use papers that are natural, renewable and recyclable products and made from wood grown in sustainable forests. The logging and manufacturing processes are expected to conform to the environmental regulations of the country of origin.

Orders: please contact Bookpoint Ltd, 130 Milton Park, Abingdon, Oxon OX14 4SB.
Telephone: (44) 01235 827720. Fax: (44) 01235 400454. Lines are open 9.00 – 5.00, Monday to Saturday, with a 24-hour message answering service.
Visit our website at www.hoddereducation.co.uk

© Catherine Berry, Diana Boynova, Tom Button, Diana Cowey, Sue de Pomerai,
Roger Porkess, 2008
First published in 2008 by
Hodder Education,
An Hachette UK Company
338 Euston Road
London NW1 3BH

Impression number   5 4 3
Year   2013 2012 2011 2010

Dynamic Learning Student Online website © Catherine Berry, Diana Boynova, Tom Button, Diana Cowey, Sue de Pomerai, Roger Porkess, 2008; with contributions from Danielle Veall; developed by Infuze Limited; cast: Tom Frankland; recorded at Alchemy Soho.

Typeset in 11/12 Helvetica by Tech-Set Ltd., Gateshead, Tyne & Wear
Printed in India

A catalogue record for this title is available from the British Library

ISBN: 978 0 340 957349

Contents

Introduction   iv

Chapter 1
Textbook
Chapter 7

Sequences and series   1
Types of sequences and series   1
A.P.s and G.P.s   6

Chapter 2
Textbook
Chapter 8
Chapter 12

Differentiation   10
Finding gradients   10
Further differentiation   14
Tangents and normals   18
Stationary points   22
Second derivatives   26

Chapter 3
Textbook
Chapter 9
Chapter 12

Integration   30
Indefinite integration   30
Finding areas by integration   34
Further areas   38
Further integration   44

Chapter 4
Textbook
Chapter 10

Trigonometry   48
Basic trigonometry   48
The sine and cosine rules   55
Radians   60
Transformations of curves   65

Chapter 5
Textbook
Chapter 11

Logarithms and exponentials   70
Logarithms and exponential functions   70
Modelling curves   75

Index   81

Formulae and results   82

Introduction

Welcome to this Revision Guide for the MEI Core 2 unit!

The book is organised into 17 sections covering the various topics in the syllabus. A typical section is four pages long; the first three pages contain essential information and key worked examples covering the topic.

The last page in each section has questions for you to answer so that you can be sure that you have really understood the topic. There is a multiple-choice exercise and an exam-style question. If you are to gain the greatest possible benefit from the book, and so do your best in the Core 2 exam, you should work through these for yourself and then refer to the accompanying website to check your answers.

The multiple-choice questions cover the basic ideas and techniques. It is really important that you work through them carefully; guessing will do you no good at all. When you have decided on the answer you think is right, enter it on the website. If you are right, it tells you so and gives the full solution; check that your answer wasn't just a fluke. If your choice is not right, the website gives you advice about your mistake; the possible wrong answers have all been designed to pick out particular common misunderstandings. The explanations on the website are based on the most likely mistakes; even if you make a different mistake, you will usually find enough help to set you on the right path so that you can try again.

When you come onto the exam-style question, write out your best possible answer. Then go to the website. You will find the solution displayed step-by-step, together with someone talking you through it and giving you helpful advice.

So the book contains the essential information to revise for the exam and, critically, also enables you to check that you have understood it properly. That is a recipe for success.

Finally, a word of warning. This book is designed to be used together with the textbook and not as a replacement for it. This Revision Guide will help you to prepare for the exam but to do really well you also need the deep understanding that comes from the detailed explanations you will find in the textbook.

Good learning and good luck!

Catherine Berry, Diana Boynova, Tom Button, Diana Cowey, Sue de Pomerai, Roger Porkess

Where you see the following icon **DL**, please refer to the Dynamic Learning Student Online website. Information on how to access this website is printed on the inside front cover of this book.

Accompanying books
MEI Structured Mathematics AS Pure Mathematics C1, C2
ISBN 978 0 340 81397 3

Companion to Advanced Mathematics and Statistics
ISBN 978 0 340 95923 7

Sequences and series

Types of sequences and series

A ABOUT THIS TOPIC

You meet sequences and series in everyday life; they often provide the patterns of events around us. In mathematics they become more and more important the further you go.

R REMEMBER

- Number patterns from GCSE.
- Solution of equations from GCSE.

K KEY FACTS

- A sequence is an ordered set of numbers $a_1, a_2, \ldots a_k, \ldots a_n$.
  For example, $1, 4, 7, 10 \ldots$

- A series is the sum of the terms of a sequence $\sum_{k=1}^{k=n} a_k = a_1 + a_2 + \ldots + a_n = S_n$.

  For example, $\sum_{k=1}^{k=5} k^2 = 1 + 4 + 9 + 16 + 25 = S_5 = 55$.

- S_n denotes the sum to n terms of the series.

- In a periodic sequence, $a_{k+p} = a_k$ for fixed integer p, called the period.
  For example, $1, 5, 25, 1, 5, 25, 1, 5, 25 \ldots$ has period 3.

- In an oscillating sequence, successive terms rise and fall below a middle value.
  For example, the sequence $a_k = (-1)^k$ is $-1, 1, -1, 1, -1, 1, \ldots$

EXAMPLE 1   Describe the sequence $2, 4, 6, 8, 2, 4, 6, 8, 2, 4, 6, 8, \ldots$

SOLUTION   This sequence repeats itself every fourth term so it is periodic with period 4.
It also oscillates between the values 2 and 8; the middle value is 5.

Terms of a sequence

There are two common ways of defining a sequence:
- As a formula such as $a_n = n^2 - 1$.

Each term can be worked out from its position in the sequence.
- In terms of the previous term, such as $a_{k+1} = 2a_k + 3$ together with a starting term, such as $a_1 = 4$.

EXAMPLE 2

A sequence is defined by $a_n = n^3 - n^2 + 1$.

Write down the first four terms of the sequence.

SOLUTION

$a_n = n^3 - n^2 + 1$

When $n = 1$ then $a_1 = 1^3 - 1^2 + 1 = 1$

When $n = 2$ then $a_2 = 2^3 - 2^2 + 1 = 8 - 4 + 1 = 5$

When $n = 3$ then $a_3 = 3^3 - 3^2 + 1 = 27 - 9 + 1 = 19$

When $n = 4$ then $a_4 = 4^3 - 4^2 + 1 = 64 - 16 + 1 = 49$

EXAMPLE 3

A sequence is defined by $a_n = 0.8a_{n-1} + 3$, $a_1 = 2$.

i) Calculate the value of a_3.

ii) What is the smallest value of n for which $a_n \geqslant 10$?

SOLUTION

i) $a_1 = 2$

$a_2 = 0.8a_1 + 3 = 0.8 \times 2 + 3 = 4.6$

$a_3 = 0.8a_2 + 3 = 0.8 \times 4.6 + 3 = 6.68$

> Notice that the differences between successive terms are growing smaller each time. Such a sequence is called 'convergent'. A convergent sequence tends to a limit as $n \to \infty$ and $a_k \to a_{k+1}$.

ii) To find the first term that is over 10, find the terms one by one.

$a_4 = 0.8a_3 + 3 = 0.8 \times 6.68 + 3 = 8.344$,

$a_5 = 0.8a_4 + 3 = 0.8 \times 8.344 + 3 = 9.6752$,

$a_6 = 0.8a_5 + 3 = 0.8 \times 9.6752 + 3 = 10.740\,16$, so $a_6 \geqslant 10$

So 6 is the smallest value of n for which $a_n \geqslant 10$.

EXAMPLE 4

A sequence is defined by $a_{k+1} = pa_k + q$ where $a_1 = 48$.

Given that $a_2 = 20$ and $a_3 = 13$, find the values of p and q.

SOLUTION

$a_2 = 20 \Rightarrow 48p + q = 20$ ①

$a_3 = 13 \Rightarrow 20p + q = 13$ ②

Subtracting ② from ① $28p = 7 \Rightarrow p = \frac{1}{4}$

Substituting $p = \frac{1}{4}$ in ① $\Rightarrow 48 \times \frac{1}{4} + q = 20$

                        $q = 8$

So $p = \frac{1}{4}$, $q = 8$.

EXAMPLE 5

The sum of n terms of a series is given by $S_n = \dfrac{n^2(n+1)^2}{4}$.

i)   Write down the first four terms of the series.

ii) Find an expression for the nth term of the series.

SOLUTION

In this example you are given the sum of the first n terms of a sequence.

i) $S_1 = a_1 = \dfrac{1^2 \times 2^2}{4} = \dfrac{4}{4} = 1 \Rightarrow a_1 = 1$

   $S_2 = a_1 + a_2 = \dfrac{2^2 \times 3^2}{4} = 9 \Rightarrow a_2 = 8$

   $S_3 = a_1 + a_2 + a_3 = \dfrac{3^2 \times 4^2}{4} = 36 \Rightarrow a_3 = 27$

   $S_4 = a_1 + a_2 + a_3 + a_4 = \dfrac{4^2 \times 5^2}{4} = 100 \Rightarrow a_4 = 64$

   So the series is $1 + 8 + 27 + 64 \ldots$

   > Notice that these are all cube numbers. You will prove this result in part **ii)**.

ii) Notice that $a_2 = S_2 - S_1$, $a_3 = S_3 - S_2$.
   In general $a_n = S_n - S_{n-1}$.

   $a_n = S_n - S_{n-1} = \dfrac{n^2(n+1)^2}{4} - \dfrac{(n-1)^2 n^2}{4}$

   $= \dfrac{n^2(n^2 + 2n + 1) - (n^2 - 2n + 1)n^2}{4}$

   $= \dfrac{n^4 + 2n^3 + n^2 - (n^4 - 2n^3 + n^2)}{4} = \dfrac{4n^3}{4}$

   The nth term of the series is n^3.

   > Check the first four terms of the series to see that this is correct.

EXAMPLE 6

A sequence is defined by $a_k = (k+1)2^k$.

Write out the series $\displaystyle\sum_{k=2}^{5} a_k$ without simplifying the terms.

SOLUTION

Looking at the terms of $\displaystyle\sum_{k=2}^{5} (k+1)2^k$ one by one

Substituting $k = 2$ into $(k+1)2^k \Rightarrow a_2 = 3 \times 2^2$
Substituting $k = 3$ into $(k+1)2^k \Rightarrow a_3 = 4 \times 2^3$
Substituting $k = 4$ into $(k+1)2^k \Rightarrow a_4 = 5 \times 2^4$
Substituting $k = 5$ into $(k+1)2^k \Rightarrow a_5 = 6 \times 2^5$

So $\displaystyle\sum_{k=2}^{5} (k+1)2^k = 3 \times 2^2 + 4 \times 2^3 + 5 \times 2^4 + 6 \times 2^5$

Series are quite often given in terms of a variable, x. The next example shows you how this can be written, and also a device for alternating the signs of the terms.

Sequences and series

EXAMPLE 7

A sequence is defined by $a_n = (-1)^n x^n$.

i) Write down the terms a_1, a_2, a_3, a_4.

A series is defined by $S_n = \sum_{k=1}^{n} (-1)^k x^k$.

ii) Write down the series S_6.

SOLUTION

i) $a_1 = (-1)^1 x^1 = -x$
$a_2 = (-1)^2 x^2 = x^2$
$a_3 = (-1)^3 x^3 = -x^3$
$a_4 = (-1)^4 x^4 = x^4$

> Why are the odd powers of x negative and the even powers of x positive?

ii) In order to write out the series you need a_5 and a_6.
$a_5 = (-1)^5 x^5 = -x^5$
$a_6 = (-1)^6 x^6 = x^6$

So $S_6 = \sum_{k=1}^{6} (-1)^k x^k = -x + x^2 - x^3 + x^4 - x^5 + x^6$

LINKS

Pure Mathematics   Method of Differences, Proof by Induction (FP1).
                    Maclaurin Series (FP2).
Statistics   Probability Distributions (S1 and S2).

Test Yourself ▷L

1 Which of the following values is the best description of the sequence whose nth term is $\cos(n \times 60°)$?

A Oscillating

B Periodic with period 6

C Both oscillating and periodic with period 6

D Neither oscillating nor periodic

2 The sum of n terms of a series is given by $S_n = \dfrac{n}{n+1}$.

Which of the following is the correct series?

A $\frac{1}{2} + \frac{2}{3} + \frac{3}{4} + \frac{4}{5} \dots$ B $\frac{1}{2} + \frac{1}{6} + \frac{1}{12} + \frac{1}{20} \dots$

C $\frac{1}{2} + \frac{1}{6} + \frac{1}{12} + \frac{1}{72} \dots$ D $\frac{1}{2} + \frac{7}{6} + \frac{17}{12} + \frac{31}{20} \dots$

3 Which one of the following statements is true?

A $\sum_{r=3}^{7} r^2 = 140$

B The sequence $1, -1, 1, -1, 1 \dots$ converges

C The sequence $1, 3, 5, 7, \dots$ is defined by $a_{k+1} = a_k + 2$

D The sum to n terms of the series $1 + \frac{1}{2} + \frac{1}{4} + \frac{1}{8} \dots$ is $2 - \left(\frac{1}{2}\right)^{n-1}$

4 Which of the following series is the same as $1 - x + 2x^2 - 3x^3 + \dots$?

A $\sum_{r=1}^{\infty} (-1)^r r x^r$ B $1 + \sum_{r=1}^{\infty} (-1)^r r x^r$

C $1 - \sum_{r=1}^{\infty} (-1)^r r x^r$ D $\sum_{r=1}^{\infty} (-1)^{r+1} r x^r$

Exam-Style Question ▷L

Jan is being treated with a special drug. At 0100 hours she is given 120 units of the drug. Each hour the amount in her body reduces by 10 units.
At 0600, 1100, and 1600 she is given subsequent doses, in each case enough to bring the amount in her body up to 120 units.
The amounts in her body, after any dose has been given, are denoted by a_1 at 0100, a_2 at 0200 and so on.

i) Write down the sequence $a_1, a_2, \ldots a_{20}$.

ii) Describe this sequence.

Jan is not given any more of the drug (she is recovering well).

iii) Write down the value of a_{21}.

iv) What is the mean amount of drug in Jan's body from 0100 to 2100?

v) What is the total amount of the drug given to Jan?

vi) When is there no drug left in Jan's body?

A.P.s and G.P.s

Arithmetic progressions (A.P.) and geometric progressions (G.P.) are probably the most commonly used sequences and series in everyday life. The ability to calculate particular terms and sums of A.P.s and G.P.s is extremely useful.

- Sequences and series from C2.

- In an arithmetic progression (A.P.) $a_{k+1} = a_k + d$ where d is a fixed number called the common difference.

- For an A.P. with first term a, common difference d and n terms:
  - The kth term $a_k = a + (k-1)d$
  - The last term, $l = a_n = a + (n-1)d$
  - The sum of n terms is $S_n = \dfrac{n}{2}(a + l) = \dfrac{n}{2}[2a + (n-1)d]$
  - In a geometric progression (G.P.) $a_{k+1} = ra_k$ where r is a fixed number called the common ratio.

- For a G.P. with first term a, common ratio r and n terms:
  - The kth term $a_k = ar^{k-1}$
  - The last term, $a_n = ar^{n-1}$
  - The sum of n terms is $S_n = a\dfrac{(r^n - 1)}{(r-1)} = a\dfrac{(1 - r^n)}{(1-r)}$
  - For an infinite G.P. to converge $-1 < r < 1$, sometimes written $|r| < 1$
  - Sum to infinity of a convergent G.P. is $S = S_\infty = \dfrac{a}{1-r}$.

In an **arithmetic progression** (A.P.) the differences between successive terms of the sequence are constant.

EXAMPLE 1

The fourth term of an A.P. is 13 and the seventh term is 19.

i) Find the first term.
ii) Find the nth term.

SOLUTION

i) Using $a_k = a + (k-1)d$ gives
fourth term $\quad a_4 = a + 3d = 13$
seventh term $\quad a_7 = a + 6d = 19$
By subtraction $\quad 6 = 3d$
Hence $d = 2$ and $a = 7$
The first term is 7

ii) The nth term is $7 + (n-1)2 = 5 + 2n$

EXAMPLE 2

i) Show that the series whose kth term is given by $a_k = 3k + 1$ is an A.P.

ii) Find the 20th term and the sum to 20 terms.

SOLUTION

i) By substitution

$a_1 = 3 \times 1 + 1 = 4$

$a_2 = 3 \times 2 + 1 = 7$

$a_3 = 3 \times 3 + 1 = 10$

> You can see that so far there is a common difference of 3. Now you need to prove that this is general.

In general $(k + 1)$th term, $a_{k+1} = 3(k+1) + 1 = 3k + 4$

$\qquad\qquad\qquad$ kth term, $\qquad\qquad\qquad\qquad\qquad\quad a_k = 3k + 1$

Difference $\qquad\qquad\qquad\qquad\qquad\quad a_{k+1} - a_k = 3$

So the sequence is an A.P. with first term 4 and common difference 3.

ii) The 20th term is $3 \times 20 + 1 = 61$.

Using $S_n = \dfrac{n}{2}(a + l)$ the sum to 20 terms is $= \dfrac{20}{2}(4 + 61) = 650$.

In a **geometric progression** (G.P.) the ratio between successive terms is constant.

EXAMPLE 3

A G.P. has second term 3 and fifth term 24.

i) Find the first term and the common ratio.

ii) Find the eighth term and the sum to 8 terms.

SOLUTION

i) Using $a_k = ar^{k-1}$ $\quad$ second term $3 = ar^{2-1} \Rightarrow ar = 3$,

$\qquad\qquad\qquad\qquad\qquad$ fifth term $24 = ar^{5-1} \Rightarrow ar^4 = 24$

So $\dfrac{ar^4}{ar} = \dfrac{24}{3}$

$\Rightarrow r^3 = 8 = 2^3$

Hence $r = 2$ and $a = 1.5$

ii) Eighth term, $a_8 = ar^{8-1} = 1.5 \times 2^7 = 192$

> Using $S_n = \dfrac{a(r^n - 1)}{(r - 1)}$.

Sum to 8 terms $S_8 = \dfrac{1.5(2^8 - 1)}{2 - 1} = 1.5 \times 255 = 382.5$

EXAMPLE 4

The fourth term of a G.P. is 4 and the sixth term is 100. Find the two possible values of the common ratio and hence the two possible values of the first term.

SOLUTION

Using $a_k = ar^{k-1}$ $\qquad$ fourth term $ar^3 = 4$,

$\qquad\qquad\qquad\qquad\qquad$ sixth term $ar^5 = 100$

Hence $\qquad\qquad \dfrac{ar^5}{ar^3} = \dfrac{100}{4}$

$\qquad\qquad\qquad\quad r^2 = 25$

Therefore $\qquad\quad r = \pm 5$

If $\qquad\qquad\quad r = +5$ then $125a = 4$ so $a = \frac{4}{125}$

Similarly if $\qquad r = -5$ then $a = -\frac{4}{125}$

> Notice that these values are paired. $a = -\frac{4}{125}$ and $r = -5$ give a different G.P.

EXAMPLE 5

i) Show that the geometric series $5 + \frac{5}{2} + \frac{5}{4} + \frac{5}{8} \ldots$ has a sum to infinity.
ii) Find the sum to infinity.

SOLUTION

i) The first term is $a = 5$.
Each successive term is half of its predecessor so $r = \frac{1}{2}$.
Since $-1 < r < 1$, the G.P. is convergent and has a sum to infinity.

ii) Sum to infinity $S = \dfrac{a}{1 - r} = \dfrac{5}{1 - \frac{1}{2}} = \dfrac{5}{\frac{1}{2}} = 10$

EXAMPLE 6

i) State the common ratio of the geometric series $3 + \dfrac{3x}{2} + \dfrac{3x^2}{4} + \dfrac{3x^3}{8} \ldots$

ii) State the restrictions on x for the series to have a sum to infinity.
iii) State the sum to infinity in terms of x.
iv) Find x if the sum to infinity is 15.

SOLUTION

i) The first term is $a = 3$
The common ratio is $r = \dfrac{x}{2}$

ii) For sum to infinity to exist $-1 < r < 1$ so in this case $-1 < \dfrac{x}{2} < 1$
Multiplying through by 2 gives $\qquad -2 < x < 2$

iii) $S = \dfrac{a}{1 - r} = \dfrac{3}{1 - \frac{x}{2}} = \dfrac{6}{2\left(1 - \frac{x}{2}\right)} = \dfrac{6}{2 - x}$

iv) Given $\dfrac{6}{2 - x} = 15$
Hence $6 = 15(2 - x) = 30 - 15x$
Hence $15x = 24$ so $x = \frac{8}{5}$ or $1\frac{3}{5}$
Notice that this satisfies $-2 < x < 2$

🔲 LINKS

Mechanics   Repeated Impacts (M2).

Test Yourself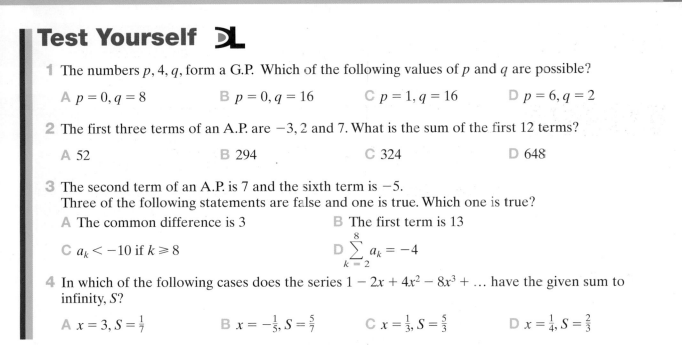

1 The numbers $p, 4, q$, form a G.P. Which of the following values of p and q are possible?

A $p = 0, q = 8$ B $p = 0, q = 16$ C $p = 1, q = 16$ D $p = 6, q = 2$

2 The first three terms of an A.P. are $-3, 2$ and 7. What is the sum of the first 12 terms?

A 52   B 294   C 324   D 648

3 The second term of an A.P. is 7 and the sixth term is -5.
Three of the following statements are false and one is true. Which one is true?

A The common difference is 3   B The first term is 13

C $a_k < -10$ if $k \geqslant 8$ D $\sum_{k=2}^{8} a_k = -4$

4 In which of the following cases does the series $1 - 2x + 4x^2 - 8x^3 + \dots$ have the given sum to infinity, S?

A $x = 3, S = \frac{1}{7}$ B $x = -\frac{1}{5}, S = \frac{5}{7}$ C $x = \frac{1}{3}, S = \frac{5}{3}$ D $x = \frac{1}{4}, S = \frac{2}{3}$

Exam-Style Question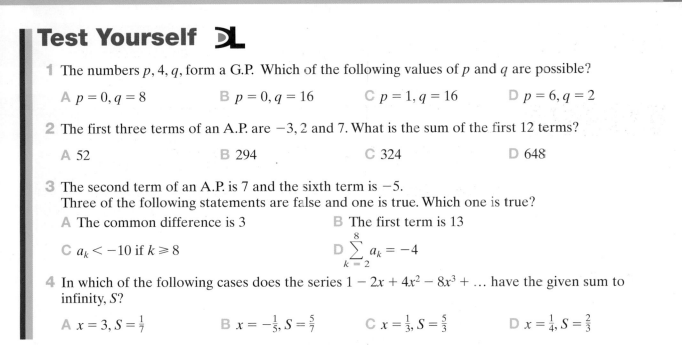

a) On Ian's first birthday his parents put £25 into a moneybox. On his second birthday they give him £28, on his third birthday £31 and so on.

i) How much money does he receive on his 18th birthday?

ii) How much money is in his moneybox at the end of his 18th birthday if none has been spent?

b) On Ian's eleventh birthday his grandparents put £200 into a bank account for him.
Compound interest at 7% is added to this account every following year on his birthday.
His grandparents add another £200 on each birthday.
How much is in his account the day after Ian is eighteen?

Differentiation

Finding gradients

You already know how to find the gradient of a straight line. The gradient of a curve is constantly changing, but you can find the gradient of a curve at any point using differentiation.

- The work on gradient from GCSE and C1.

- The gradient of a curve at a point is the gradient of the tangent at that point.
- The gradient of the tangent to a curve is given by the limit of the gradient of a chord.
- The gradient function $\frac{dy}{dx}$ gives the gradient of the curve, and measures the rate of change of y with respect to x.
- The gradient function of $y = kx^n$ is given by $\frac{dy}{dx} = knx^{n-1}$.
- The gradient function of a constant function $y = c$ is $\frac{dy}{dx} = 0$.

The gradient of a curve

The gradient of a curve changes as you move along it. At any point on the curve, the gradient of the curve is the gradient of the tangent to the curve at that point.

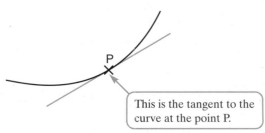

This is the tangent to the curve at the point P.

A chord is a line joining two points on a curve. The diagram shows a chord from the point P on a curve to another point, A, close to P. The gradient of the chord PA is an approximation to the gradient of the tangent at P.

You can get a better approximation for the gradient of the tangent at P by using the chord from P to another point B, closer to P than A.

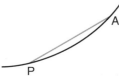

By choosing points closer and closer to point P, you can find chords whose gradients get closer and closer to the gradient of the tangent at P.

The gradient of the tangent at P is the **limit** of the gradient of the chord PA, as the point A approaches the point P.

The gradient function

The gradient function for a curve is a function which tells you the gradient of a curve at any point. The gradient function for a curve is often written as $\frac{dy}{dx}$.

For example, for the curve $y = x^2$, the gradient function is given by $\frac{dy}{dx} = 2x$.

This means that at the point where $x = 1$, the gradient of the curve is 2; at the point where $x = 2$, the gradient of the curve is 4, and so on.

In general, for the curve $y = x^n$, the gradient function is given by $\frac{dy}{dx} = nx^{n-1}$.

EXAMPLE 1   Find the gradient of the curve $y = x^3$ at the point where $x = 2$.

SOLUTION

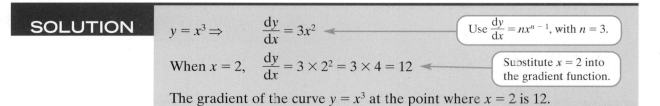

$y = x^3 \Rightarrow \qquad \frac{dy}{dx} = 3x^2$ ⟵ Use $\frac{dy}{dx} = nx^{n-1}$, with $n = 3$.

When $x = 2$, $\quad \frac{dy}{dx} = 3 \times 2^2 = 3 \times 4 = 12$ ⟵ Substitute $x = 2$ into the gradient function.

The gradient of the curve $y = x^3$ at the point where $x = 2$ is 12.

Differentiation

The gradient function is sometimes called the **derivative**.

As well as telling you the gradient of a curve, the derivative $\frac{dy}{dx}$ tells you the rate of change of y with respect to x.

The process of finding a derivative is called **differentiation**.

Differentiating using standard results

The standard result: $\quad y = x^n \Rightarrow \frac{dy}{dx} = nx^{n-1}$

can be extended to include functions of the form $y = kx^n$, where k is a constant.

$$y = kx^n \Rightarrow \frac{dy}{dx} = knx^{n-1}$$

Notice in particular the important case when $n = 0$, which gives the result

$$y = k \Rightarrow \frac{dy}{dx} = 0$$

This makes sense, since the graph $y = k$ is a horizontal straight line, which has gradient zero at all points.

EXAMPLE 2

Differentiate the following functions:

i) $y = 2x^5$ ii) $y = \frac{1}{2}x^{10}$ iii) $y = 3$

SOLUTION

i) $y = 2x^5 \Rightarrow \dfrac{dy}{dx} = 2 \times 5x^4 = 10x^4$ Using the standard result with $n = 5$.

ii) $y = \frac{1}{2}x^{10} \Rightarrow \dfrac{dy}{dx} = \frac{1}{2} \times 10x^9 = 5x^9$ Using the standard result with $n = 10$.

iii) $y = 3 \Rightarrow \dfrac{dy}{dx} = 0$ 3 is a constant so its derivative is zero.

Differentiating sums and differences of functions

To differentiate the sum or difference of two or more functions, you differentiate each term separately and then add or subtract the results as appropriate.

EXAMPLE 3

Find the gradient of the function $y = x^4 - 3x^2 + x + 2$ at the point $(2, 8)$.

SOLUTION

$y = x^4 - 3x^2 + x + 2 \Rightarrow \dfrac{dy}{dx} = 4x^3 - (3 \times 2x) + 1 + 0 = 4x^3 - 6x + 1$

When $x = 2$, $\dfrac{dy}{dx} = (4 \times 2^3) - (6 \times 2) + 1 = 21$ Notice that the derivative of x is 1 and the derivative of 2 is zero.

The gradient of the curve at the point $(2, 8)$ is 21.

EXAMPLE 4

Find the co-ordinates of the point(s) on the curve $y = x^3 - 3x^2 - 8x + 4$ at which the gradient of the curve is 1.

SOLUTION

$y = x^3 - 3x^2 - 8x + 4 \Rightarrow \dfrac{dy}{dx} = 3x^2 - 6x - 8$

At the point for which the gradient is 1: $3x^2 - 6x - 8 = 1$
$$3x^2 - 6x - 9 = 0$$
$$x^2 - 2x - 3 = 0$$
$$(x - 3)(x + 1) = 0$$
$$x = 3 \text{ or } x = -1$$

Substitute the x co-ordinates into the equation of the curve to find the y co-ordinates.

When $x = 3$, $y = 3^3 - 3 \times 3^2 - 8 \times 3 + 4 = -20$

When $x = -1$, $y = (-1)^3 - 3 \times (-1)^2 - 8 \times (-1) + 4 = 8$

The points at which the gradient of the curve is 1 are $(3, -20)$ and $(-1, 8)$.

□ LINKS

Pure Mathematics   Differentiation is developed further in C3, and used extensively throughout pure mathematics.

Mechanics   Kinematics (M1).

Differentiation

Test Yourself ▷L

1 Differentiate $y = x^4 - 2x^3 - x + 3$.

   A $\dfrac{dy}{dx} = 4x^3 - 6x^2 + 2$ **B** $\dfrac{dy}{dx} = 4x^3 - 6x^2$ **C** $\dfrac{dy}{dx} = 4x^3 - 6x^2 + 3$

   D $y = 4x^3 - 5x^2 - 1$ **E** $\dfrac{dy}{dx} = 4x^3 - 6x^2 - 1$

2 Find the gradient of the tangent to the curve $y = 4 - 3x - x^2 + 2x^3$ at the point for which $x = -2$.

   A 31   **B** 25   **C** 29   **D** -23 **E** 21

3 Find the gradient of the curve $y = 3x^2 - 5x - 1$ at the point $(2, 1)$.

   A 5   **B** 7   **C** 6   **D** 1   **E** -1

4 Find the co-ordinates of the point on the curve $y = 4 - 3x + x^2$ at which the tangent to the curve has gradient -1.

   A $(1, 2)$ **B** $(1, -1)$ **C** $(-2, 14)$ **D** $(-2, -1)$

5 Find the gradient of the curve $y = x^5(2x + 1)$ at the point at which $x = -1$.

   A 10   **B** -3 **C** -7 **D** -17 **E** 7

Exam-Style Question ▷L

A is the point on the curve $y = 2x^2 - x + 1$ with x co-ordinate 2.
B is the point on the same curve with x co-ordinate 2.1.

i) Calculate the gradient of the chord AB of the curve.

ii) Give the x co-ordinate of a point C on the curve for which the gradient of chord AC is a better approximation to the gradient of the curve at A.

iii) Find the gradient of the curve at A by differentiation.

Further differentiation

A ABOUT THIS TOPIC

This section extends the work on differentiation to include expressions involving negative and fractional powers of x.

R REMEMBER

- Indices from C1.
- Basic differentiation from C2.

K KEY FACTS

- The gradient function of $y = kx^n$ is given by $\dfrac{dy}{dx} = knx^{n-1}$.

  This is true for all values of n, including negative and fractional values.

Differentiation using standard results

The standard result

$$y = kx^n \Rightarrow \frac{dy}{dx} = knx^{n-1}$$

is true for all values of n.

This means that you can apply it to expressions involving negative or fractional powers of x.

Differentiating negative powers of x

When differentiating a negative power of x, you use the standard result in the same way that you do for a positive power of x.

EXAMPLE 1   Find the gradient function for the curve $y = x^{-3}$.

SOLUTION $y = x^{-3} \Rightarrow \dfrac{dy}{dx} = -3x^{-4} = -\dfrac{3}{x^4}$

> The value of n is -3, so the value of $n - 1$ is -4.

Remember from C1 that $\dfrac{1}{x^n} = x^{-n}$.

So $y = x^{-3}$ is the same as $y = \dfrac{1}{x^3}$ and the answer $\dfrac{dy}{dx} = -3x^{-4}$ is the same

as $\dfrac{dy}{dx} = -\dfrac{3}{x^4}$.

A ADVICE

If you need to differentiate a function of the form $\dfrac{k}{x^n}$, write it as kx^{-n} first.

EXAMPLE 2

EXAMPLE 2   Find the gradient of the curve $y = \dfrac{3}{x^2}$ at the point where $x = 2$.

SOLUTION

$$y = \frac{3}{x^2} = 3x^{-2} \Rightarrow \frac{dy}{dx} = 3 \times -2x^{-3} = -6x^{-3}$$

When $x = 2$, $\dfrac{dy}{dx} = -6 \times 2^{-3} = \dfrac{-6}{2^3} = -\dfrac{6}{8} = -\dfrac{3}{4}$

The gradient of the curve at the point where $x = 2$ is $-\frac{3}{4}$.

You can differentiate sums and differences of functions by differentiating one term at a time, just as you did in the last section.

EXAMPLE 3   Differentiate the function $y = \dfrac{1}{x} - \dfrac{2}{x^4} + 3$.

SOLUTION

$$y = \frac{1}{x} - \frac{2}{x^4} + 3 = x^{-1} - 2x^{-4} + 3$$

> Rewrite the function using negative indices.

$$\frac{dy}{dx} = -1x^{-2} - 2 \times -4x^{-5} + 0$$

> Differentiate each term. Be careful with signs.

$$= -x^{-2} + 8x^{-5}$$

$$= -\frac{1}{x^2} + \frac{8}{x^5}$$

> If you want to you can write the final expression using fractions.

Differentiating fractional powers of x

When differentiating a fractional power of x, you use the standard result in the same way that you do for an integer power of x.

EXAMPLE 4   Differentiate the function $y = x^{\frac{2}{3}}$.

SOLUTION

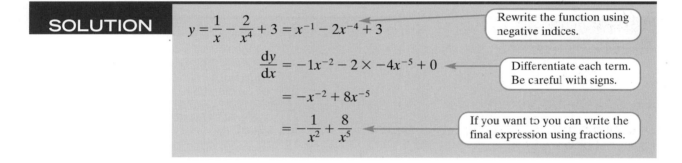

$$y = x^{\frac{2}{3}} \Rightarrow \frac{dy}{dx} = \frac{2}{3}x^{-\frac{1}{3}}$$

> The value of n is $\frac{2}{3}$, so the value of $n - 1$ is $\frac{2}{3} - 1 = -\frac{1}{3}$.

Remember from C1 that $x^{\frac{1}{n}} = \sqrt[n]{x}$.

So $y = x^{\frac{2}{3}}$ is $y = \sqrt[3]{x^2}$ and the answer $\dfrac{dy}{dx} = \dfrac{2}{3}x^{-\frac{1}{3}} = \dfrac{2}{3} \times \dfrac{1}{\sqrt[3]{x}} = \dfrac{2}{3\sqrt[3]{x}}$.

A ADVICE

If you need to differentiate a function involving a root, write it using a fractional index first.

For example, write $\sqrt[3]{x}$ as $x^{\frac{1}{3}}$, and $\dfrac{1}{\sqrt{x}}$ as $x^{-\frac{1}{2}}$.

2 Differentiation

EXAMPLE 5 Find the gradient of the curve $y = 2\sqrt{x^3}$ at the point at which $x = 4$.

SOLUTION

$$y = 2\sqrt{x^3} \qquad = 2x^{\frac{3}{2}}$$

> $\sqrt{x^3} = (x^3)^{\frac{1}{2}} = x^{\frac{3}{2}}$.

$$\frac{dy}{dx} = 2 \times \tfrac{3}{2}x^{\frac{1}{2}}$$

$$= 3x^{\frac{1}{2}}$$

$$= 3\sqrt{x}$$

> If you want to, you can write the final expression using a square root. This may make it easier if you need to substitute in a value for x.

When $x = 4$, $\dfrac{dy}{dx} = 3\sqrt{4} = 3 \times 2 = 6$

The gradient of the curve at the point at which $x = 4$ is 6.

EXAMPLE 6 Differentiate the function $y = \sqrt[3]{x} - \dfrac{4}{\sqrt{x}}$.

SOLUTION

$$y = \sqrt[3]{x} - \frac{4}{\sqrt{x}}$$

> Rewrite the expression using fractional indices.

$$= x^{\frac{1}{3}} - 4x^{-\frac{1}{2}}$$

> Differentiate each term. Be careful with signs

$$\frac{dy}{dx} = \tfrac{1}{3}x^{-\frac{2}{3}} - 4 \times -\tfrac{1}{2}x^{-\frac{3}{2}}$$

$$= \tfrac{1}{3}x^{-\frac{2}{3}} + 2x^{-\frac{3}{2}}$$

> You could write this expression using roots, but it is fine to leave it as it is.

EXAMPLE 7 Find the gradient function of the curve $y = \dfrac{1}{2x^3} - 3\sqrt{x} + x^2 - 2x$.

SOLUTION

$$y = \frac{1}{2x^3} - 3\sqrt{x} + x^2 - 2x$$

$$= \tfrac{1}{2}x^{-3} - 3x^{\frac{1}{2}} + x^2 - 2x$$

$$\frac{dy}{dx} = \tfrac{1}{2} \times -3x^{-4} - 3 \times \tfrac{1}{2}x^{-\frac{1}{2}} + 2x - 2$$

$$= -\tfrac{3}{2}x^{-4} - \tfrac{3}{2}x^{-\frac{1}{2}} + 2x - 2$$

$$= -\frac{3}{2x^4} - \frac{3}{2\sqrt{x}} + 2x - 2$$

LINKS

Pure Mathematics   Differentiation is developed further in C3, and used extensively throughout pure mathematics.

Mechanics   Kinematics (M1).

Differentiation

Test Yourself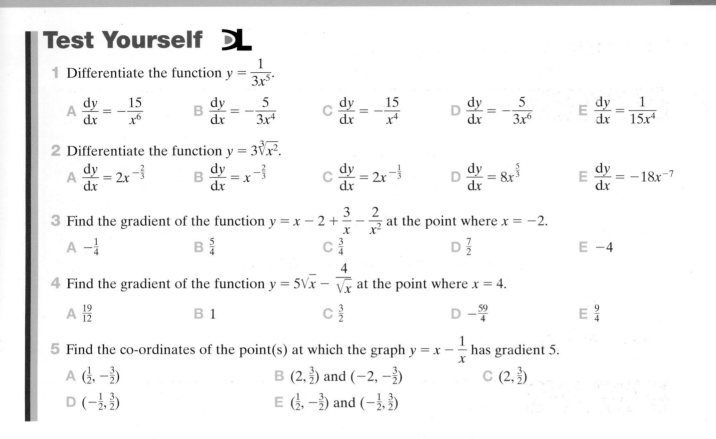

1 Differentiate the function $y = \dfrac{1}{3x^5}$.

  A $\dfrac{dy}{dx} = -\dfrac{15}{x^6}$ B $\dfrac{dy}{dx} = -\dfrac{5}{3x^4}$ C $\dfrac{dy}{dx} = -\dfrac{15}{x^4}$ D $\dfrac{dy}{dx} = -\dfrac{5}{3x^6}$ E $\dfrac{dy}{dx} = \dfrac{1}{15x^4}$

2 Differentiate the function $y = 3\sqrt[3]{x^2}$.

  A $\dfrac{dy}{dx} = 2x^{-\frac{2}{3}}$ B $\dfrac{dy}{dx} = x^{-\frac{2}{3}}$ C $\dfrac{dy}{dx} = 2x^{-\frac{1}{3}}$ D $\dfrac{dy}{dx} = 8x^{\frac{5}{3}}$ E $\dfrac{dy}{dx} = -18x^{-7}$

3 Find the gradient of the function $y = x - 2 + \dfrac{3}{x} - \dfrac{2}{x^2}$ at the point where $x = -2$.

  A $-\dfrac{1}{4}$ B $\dfrac{5}{4}$ C $\dfrac{3}{4}$ D $\dfrac{7}{2}$ E -4

4 Find the gradient of the function $y = 5\sqrt{x} - \dfrac{4}{\sqrt{x}}$ at the point where $x = 4$.

  A $\dfrac{19}{12}$ B 1 C $\dfrac{3}{2}$ D $-\dfrac{59}{4}$ E $\dfrac{9}{4}$

5 Find the co-ordinates of the point(s) at which the graph $y = x - \dfrac{1}{x}$ has gradient 5.

  A $\left(\frac{1}{2}, -\frac{3}{2}\right)$ B $\left(2, \frac{3}{2}\right)$ and $\left(-2, -\frac{3}{2}\right)$ C $\left(2, \frac{3}{2}\right)$

  D $\left(-\frac{1}{2}, \frac{3}{2}\right)$ E $\left(\frac{1}{2}, -\frac{3}{2}\right)$ and $\left(-\frac{1}{2}, \frac{3}{2}\right)$

Exam-Style Question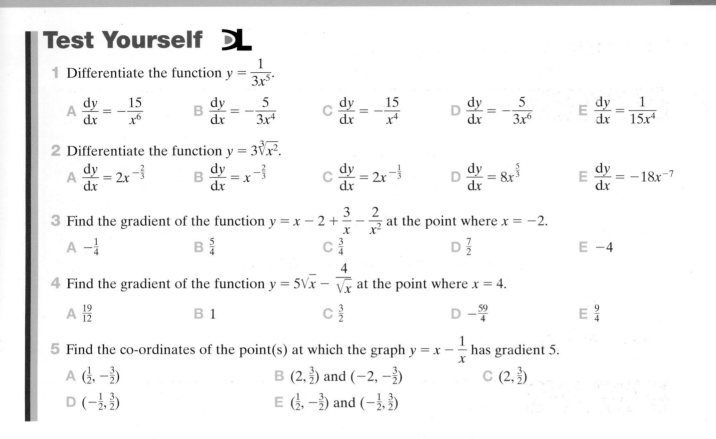

a) Differentiate $x - \dfrac{3}{x^4} + \dfrac{2}{x^5}$.

b) Differentiate $3x^2 - 2\sqrt{x^5} + \dfrac{1}{\sqrt[3]{x}}$.

Tangents and normals

You have already seen that you can use differentiation to find the gradient of the tangent to a curve at any point. You can use this knowledge to find the equation of the tangent. A straight line which passes through a curve at right angles to the tangent is called a normal to the curve, and you can also find the equation of a normal.

- Differentiation from C2.
- The equation of a straight line from its gradient and a point on the line from C1.
- The rule that if two lines with gradients m_1 and m_2 are perpendicular, then $m_1m_2 = -1$, from C1.

- You can find the gradient, m_1, of a tangent to a curve at a given point using differentiation.

- The equation of the tangent to a curve at the point (x_1, y_1) is given by $y - y_1 = m_1(x - x_1)$.

- The gradient, m_2, of a normal to a curve at a given point can be found by first finding the gradient m_1, of the tangent, and then using the relationship $m_1m_2 = -1$.

- The equation of the normal to a curve at the point (x_1, y_1) is given by $y - y_1 = m_2(x - x_1)$.

The equation of a tangent to a curve

In C1 you found the equation of a straight line with gradient m_1 and passing through the point (x_1, y_1) using

$$y - y_1 = m_1(x - x_1).$$

You can use this to find the equation of a tangent to a curve at a given point.

First, you need to find the value of m_1. You do this by differentiating the equation of the curve and substituting the value of x_1 into your

expression for 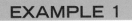 $\dfrac{dy}{dx}$. This is shown in Example 1.

EXAMPLE 1   The diagram shows the curve $y = x^2 - x + 1$ and the tangent at the point $(2, 3)$.

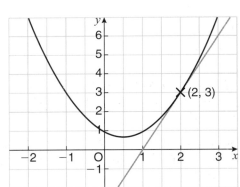

Find the equation of this tangent.

SOLUTION

$$y = x^2 - x + 1 \Rightarrow \frac{dy}{dx} = 2x - 1$$

> Differentiate to find the gradient function.

When $x = 2$, $\quad \dfrac{dy}{dx} = 2 \times 2 - 1 = 4 - 1 = 3.$

> Substitute $x = 2$ to find the gradient of the tangent.

The tangent has gradient 3 and passes through the point $(2, 3)$.
So the equation of the tangent is $y - 3 = 3(x - 2)$
$$y - 3 = 3x - 6$$
$$y = 3x - 3$$

> Find the equation of the tangent.

The equation of a normal to a curve

The normal to a curve at a given point is the straight line which is perpendicular to the tangent at that point. For example, the diagram shows the curve $y = 4x - x^2$ and the tangent and normal at the point $(1, 3)$.

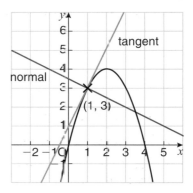

You can work out the gradient of the normal by first using differentiation to work out the gradient of the tangent. Since the tangent and the normal are perpendicular lines, their gradients must satisfy the relationship $m_1 m_2 = -1$. The normal passes through the point $(1, 3)$, so you can find the equation of the normal from the gradient and the co-ordinates of this point. Example 2 shows how this is done.

EXAMPLE 2

Find the equation of the normal to the curve $y = 4x - x^2$ at the point $(1, 3)$.

> $x_1 = 1, y_1 = 3.$

SOLUTION

$$y = 4x - x^2 \Rightarrow \frac{dy}{dx} = 4 - 2x$$

> Differentiate to find the gradient function.

When $x = 1$, the gradient m_1 of the tangent is $m_1 = 4 - 2 \times 1 = 2$.

> Substitute $x = 1$ to find the gradient of the tangent.

The gradient m_2 of the normal is $\qquad m_2 = -\dfrac{1}{m_1} = -\dfrac{1}{2}.$

The normal has gradient $-\frac{1}{2}$ and passes through the point $(1, 3)$.

So the equation of the normal is $y - y_1 = m_2(x - x_1)$

> Find the gradient of the normal.

$$y - 3 = -\tfrac{1}{2}(x - 1)$$
$$2y - 6 = -x + 1$$
$$2y + x = 7$$

> Find the equation of the normal.

⚠️ Sometimes you may only be given x_1, the x co-ordinate of the point at which you need to find a tangent or normal. If this is the case, you will need to find y_1 before you can use $y - y_1 = m(x - x_1)$.

Don't mix up the equation of the curve and the gradient function. If you want to find the y co-ordinate of the point on the curve, make sure you use the equation of the curve and not the gradient function!

EXAMPLE 3

Find the equations of the tangent and normal to the curve $y = x^3 - 2x^2 - 5x + 7$ at the point where $x = 2$.

SOLUTION

When $x = 2$, $y = 2^3 - 2 \times 2^2 - 5 \times 2 + 7 = 8 - 8 - 10 + 7 = -3$, so the point is $(2, -3)$. ◄───── *Find the y co-ordinate of the point where $x = 2$.*

$x_1 = 2$, $y_1 = -3$

$y = x^3 - 2x^2 - 5x + 7 \Rightarrow \dfrac{dy}{dx} = 3x^2 - 4x - 5$ ◄───── *Differentiate to find the gradient function.*

Substitute $x = 2$ to find the gradient of the tangent. ─────►

When $x = 2$, the gradient m_1 of the tangent is
$m_1 = 3 \times 2^2 - 4 \times 2 - 5 = 12 - 8 - 5 = -1$
So the tangent has gradient -1 and passes through the point $(2, -3)$.

The equation of the tangent is
$$y - y_1 = m_1(x - x_1)$$ ◄───── *Find the equation of the tangent.*
$$y - (-3) = -(x - 2)$$
$$y + 3 = -x + 2$$
$$y + x + 1 = 0$$

Find the gradient of the normal. ─────►

The gradient m_2 of the normal is $m_2 = -\dfrac{1}{m_1} = -\dfrac{1}{-1} = 1$.

The normal has gradient 1 and passes through the point $(2, -3)$.

So the equation of the normal is
$$y - y_1 = m_2(x - x_1)$$
$$y - (-3) = 1(x - 2)$$
$$y + 3 = x - 2$$
$$y = x - 5$$

Find the equation of the normal.

LINKS

This work extends the co-ordinate geometry introduced in C1.
It is used in the Investigating Curves topic in FP2.

Test Yourself ▷L

1 Find the gradient of the normal to the curve $y = \dfrac{4}{\sqrt{x}}$ at the point where $x = 4$.

   A $-\dfrac{1}{4}$ B -4 C 4 D 3 E -1

2 Find the equation of the tangent to the curve $y = x^3 - 3x^2 + x + 4$ at the point where $x = 1$.

   A $y + 2x = 5$ B $y + 2x = 1$ C $y = -2x$

   D $y + 2x = 7$ E $y = 2x + 3$

3 Find the equation of the normal to the curve $y = x^2 + 7x + 6$ at the point where $x = -2$.

   A $y = 3x + 2$ B $3y + 10 = x$ C $3y + x + 38 = 0$

   D $y + 6 = 3x$ E $3y + x + 14 = 0$

4 Find the equation of the tangent to the curve $y = \sqrt{x}$ at the point where $x = 4$.

   A $4y = x - 8$ B $y + x = 6$ C $4y = x + 8$ D $4y = x - 2$ E $4y = x + 4$

5 Find the equation of the normal to the curve $y = \dfrac{1}{x}$ at the point where $x = 2$.

   A $y + x = 4$ B $2y = 8x - 15$ C $2y + 8x = 17$

   D $4y = x$ E $2y = 8x - 17$

Exam-Style Question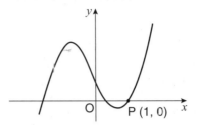

The diagram shows the cubic curve with equation $y = 2x^3 - 3x + 1$.

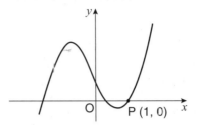

i)   Show that the tangent to the curve at the point P $(1, 0)$ has gradient 3.

ii) Find the co-ordinates of the other point, Q, on the curve at which the tangent has gradient 3.

iii) Find the equation of the normal to the curve at Q.

Stationary points

K **KEY FACTS**

- Stationary points on a curve are points at which the gradient of the curve is zero.
- A stationary point can be:
  - a local maximum, at which the gradient changes from positive to negative
  - a local minimum, at which the gradient changes from negative to positive
  - a stationary point of inflection, in which the gradient has the same sign on both sides of the stationary point.
- The nature of a stationary point can be found by considering the sign of the gradient on either side of the point.

Stationary points

A stationary point on a curve is a point at which the gradient of the curve is zero. This means that the tangent to the curve is horizontal. There are three different types of stationary point.

- A local maximum point, in which the gradient is positive to the left of the point and negative to the right of the point.

- A local minimum point, in which the gradient is negative to the left of the point and positive to the right of the point.

- A stationary point of inflection, in which the gradient is the same on both sides of the stationary point.

Finding stationary points

You can find stationary points on a curve by differentiating the equation of the curve and finding the points at which the gradient function is zero.

You can determine the nature of stationary points by finding the gradient of the curve on either side of the stationary point.

A ADVICE

It is a good idea to set your work out in a table, as shown in Example 1.

EXAMPLE 1

i) Find the co-ordinates of the stationary points on the curve
$y = x^3 - 3x^2 - 9x + 10$.
ii) Find the nature of the stationary points.
iii) Sketch the curve.

SOLUTION

i) $y = x^3 - 3x^2 - 9x + 10 \Rightarrow \dfrac{dy}{dx} = 3x^2 - 6x - 9$

At stationary points, $\dfrac{dy}{dx} = 0$, so $3x^2 - 6x - 9 = 0$

$x^2 - 2x - 3 = 0$ ← Divide through by 3.

$(x - 3)(x + 1) = 0$

$x = 3$ or $x = -1$

When $x = 3$, $\quad y = 3^3 - 3 \times 3^2 - 9 \times 3 + 10 = -17$
When $x = -1$, $\quad y = (-1)^3 - 3(-1)^2 - 9(-1) + 10 = 15$
The stationary points are $(3, -17)$ and $(-1, 15)$.

> You need to find the sign of the gradient at one point to the left of $(-1, 15)$, one point in between the two stationary points, and one point to the right of $(3, -17)$

ii) At the point where $x = -2$ $\quad \dfrac{dy}{dx} = 3(-2)^2 - 6(-2) - 9 = 15 > 0$

At the point where $x = 0$ $\quad \dfrac{dy}{dx} = 3 \times 0 - 6 \times 0 - 9 = -9 < 0$

At the point where $x = 4$ $\quad \dfrac{dy}{dx} = 3 \times 4^2 - 6 \times 4 - 9 = 15 > 0$

	$x < -1$	$x = -1$	$-1 < x < 3$	$x = 3$	$x > 3$
Sign of $\dfrac{dy}{dx}$	+ve ╱	0 ──	−ve ╲	0 ──	+ve ╱
Stationary point		Local maximum		Local minimum	

The stationary point $(-1, 15)$ is a local maximum point, and $(3, -17)$ is a local minimum point.

iii)

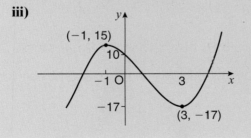

Be careful if there is more than one stationary point close together. For example, if there are stationary points at $x = \frac{1}{2}$ and $x = 1$, then you can't use $x = 0$ to look at the gradient on the left of the point $x = 1$. You need to use a point between $x = \frac{1}{2}$ and $x = 1$, such as $x = \frac{3}{4}$.

EXAMPLE 2

i) Find the co-ordinates of the stationary points on the curve $y = 3x^4 - 4x^3 + 2$ and determine their nature.

ii) Sketch the curve.

SOLUTION

i) $y = 3x^4 - 4x^3 + 2 \Rightarrow \dfrac{dy}{dx} = 12x^3 - 12x^2$

At stationary points, $\dfrac{dy}{dx} = 0$, so $12x^3 - 12x^2 = 0$

$$x^3 - x^2 = 0 \quad \longleftarrow \text{Divide through by 12.}$$
$$x^2(x - 1) = 0$$
$$x = 0 \text{ or } x = 1$$

When $x = 0$, $\quad y = 3 \times 0 - 4 \times 0 + 2 = 2$

When $x = 1$, $\quad y = 3 \times 1^4 - 4 \times 1^3 + 2 = 3 - 4 + 2 = 1$

The stationary points are $(0, 2)$ and $(1, 1)$.

At the point where $x = -1$, $\dfrac{dy}{dx} = 12(-1)^3 - 12(-1)^2 = -24 < 0$

At the point where $x = \frac{1}{2}$, $\dfrac{dy}{dx} = 12(\frac{1}{2})^3 - 12(\frac{1}{2})^2 = -1.5 < 0$

At the point where $x = 2$, $\dfrac{dy}{dx} = 12 \times 2^3 - 12 \times 2^2 = 48 > 0$

	$x < 0$	$x = 0$	$0 < x < 1$	$x = 1$	$x > 1$
Sign of $\dfrac{dy}{dx}$	−ve \	0 —	−ve \	0 —	+ve /
Stationary point		Point of Inflection		Local minimum	

The stationary point $(0, 2)$ is a point of inflection, and $(1, 1)$ is a local minimum point.

ii)

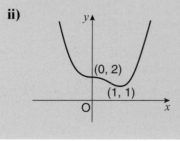

(0, 2)

(1, 1)

LINKS

This work has applications throughout Pure Mathematics and Mechanics.

Test Yourself ▷L

1 Find the co-ordinates of the stationary point(s) on the curve $y = x^3 - 3x^2 - 9x + 11$.

  A $(1, 0)$ and $(-3, -16)$ B $(-1, 0)$ and $(3, 0)$ C $(-1, 16)$ and $(3, -16)$

  D $(1, -12)$ and $(-3, 36)$ E $(1, 0)$ only

2 Find the co-ordinates of the stationary point(s) on the curve $y = 3x^4 + 2x^3 + 1$.

  A $(-\frac{1}{2}, \frac{15}{16})$ only   B $(0, 1)$ and $(-\frac{1}{2}, \frac{9}{15})$ C $(-\frac{1}{2}, \frac{9}{16})$ only

  D $(0, 1)$ and $(-\frac{1}{2}, \frac{15}{16})$ E $(0, 1)$ and $(\frac{1}{2}, \frac{23}{16})$

3 The curve $y = x^3 - 2x^2 + x$ has stationary points at $(\frac{1}{3}, \frac{4}{27})$ and $(1, 0)$.
What is the nature of these stationary points?

  A $(\frac{1}{3}, \frac{4}{27})$ is a stationary point of inflection, and $(1, 0)$ is a stationary point of inflection.

  B $(\frac{1}{3}, \frac{4}{27})$ is a local maximum point, and $(1, 0)$ is a local minimum point.

  C $(\frac{1}{3}, \frac{4}{27})$ is a local minimum point, and $(1, 0)$ is a local maximum point.

  D $(\frac{1}{3}, \frac{4}{27})$ is a local maximum point, and $(1, 0)$ is a stationary point of inflection.

  E $(\frac{1}{3}, \frac{4}{27})$ is a stationary point of inflection, and $(1, 0)$ is a local minimum point.

4 The curve $y = 3x^4 - 8x^3 + 6x^2 + 3$ has stationary points at $(0, 3)$ and $(1, 4)$.
What is the nature of these stationary points?

  A $(0, 3)$ is a local minimum point and $(1, 4)$ is a stationary point of inflection.

  B $(0, 3)$ is a stationary point of inflection and $(1, 4)$ is a local maximum point.

  C $(0, 3)$ is a local maximum point and $(1, 4)$ is a stationary point of inflection.

  D $(0, 3)$ is a stationary point of inflection and $(1, 4)$ is a local minimum point.

  E $(0, 3)$ is a local minimum point and $(1, 4)$ is a local maximum point.

5 The curves $y = x^5$ and $y = x^6$ each have a stationary point at the origin.
Which one of the statements below is true?

  A For both curves, the origin is a stationary point of inflection.

  B For the curve $y = x^5$, the origin is a stationary point of inflection, and for the curve $y = x^6$, the origin is a local maximum point.

  C For the curve $y = x^5$, the origin is a local minimum point, and for the curve $y = x^6$, the origin is a local maximum point.

  D For the curve $y = x^5$, the origin is a stationary point of inflection, and for the curve $y = x^6$, the origin is a local minimum point.

Exam-Style Question ▷L

A curve has equation $y = 3x^4 - 8x^3 + 5$.

i) Use calculus to find the co-ordinates of the stationary points of this curve.
Determine also the nature of these stationary points.

ii) Sketch the curve.

Second derivatives

K **KEY FACTS**

- A function is increasing if the gradient function is positive. If the gradient function is positive everywhere, the function is called an increasing function.

- A function is decreasing if the gradient function is negative. If the gradient function is negative everywhere, the function is called a decreasing function.

- The second derivative is found by differentiating the gradient function $\frac{dy}{dx}$. It is written as $\frac{d^2y}{dx^2}$.

- At a stationary point:
  - if the second derivative is positive, the stationary point is a local minimum
  - if the second derivative is negative, the stationary point is a local maximum
  - if the second derivative is zero, the stationary point could be a local minimum, a local maximum or a stationary point of inflection. You need to look at the gradient on either side to find out the nature of the stationary point.

Increasing and decreasing functions

A function is increasing if y increases as x increases. If a function is increasing, then the gradient must be positive.

A function is decreasing if y decreases as x increases. If a function is decreasing, then the gradient must be negative.

Many functions are increasing functions for some values of x, and decreasing functions for other values of x.

If a function is increasing for all values of x, it is called an increasing function.

If a function is decreasing for all values of x, it is called a decreasing function.

This is an increasing function

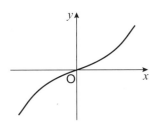

This is a decreasing function

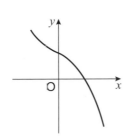

This function is decreasing for negative values of x, and increasing for positive values of x.

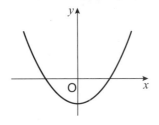

EXAMPLE 1

Find the range of values of x for which the function $y = x^3 - 3x + 1$ is an increasing function of x.

SOLUTION

$y = x^3 - 3x + 1 \Rightarrow \dfrac{dy}{dx} = 3x^2 - 3$

The function is increasing if $\dfrac{dy}{dx} > 0$

$$3x^2 - 3 > 0$$
$$x^2 - 1 > 0$$
$$(x - 1)(x + 1) > 0$$

The sketch of the graph of $\dfrac{dy}{dx} = x^2 - 1$ shows that the solution to this inequality is $x < -1$ or $x > 1$.

The function is increasing for $x < -1$ or $x > 1$.

> Notice that a function is neither increasing nor decreasing if the gradient function is zero.

The second derivative

If you differentiate the gradient function of a function, the result is called the second derivative of the function. To find the second derivative of a function, you differentiate the function twice. The second derivative of a function $y = f(x)$ is written as $\dfrac{d^2y}{dx^2}$.

The second derivative tells you the rate of change of the gradient function.

EXAMPLE 2

Find the second derivative of the function $y = x^4 - 3x^2 - 2x + \dfrac{1}{x}$.

SOLUTION

$y = x^4 - 3x^2 - 2x + x^{-1}$

Differentiate to give the gradient function: $\dfrac{dy}{dx} = 4x^3 - 6x - 2 - x^{-2}$

Differentiate again to give the second derivative: $\dfrac{d^2y}{dx^2} = 12x^2 - 6 - 0 + 2x^{-3}$

$$= 12x^2 - 6 + \dfrac{2}{x^3}$$

EXAMPLE 3

A curve has equation $y = x^3 - x^2 - 3x - 1$.

Find the values of $\dfrac{dy}{dx}$ and $\dfrac{d^2y}{dx^2}$ at the point where $x = -2$.

SOLUTION

$y = x^3 - x^2 - 3x - 1 \Rightarrow \dfrac{dy}{dx} = 3x^2 - 2x - 3 \Rightarrow \dfrac{d^2y}{dx^2} = 6x - 2$

When $x = -2$, $\dfrac{dy}{dx} = 3 \times (-2)^2 - 2 \times (-2) - 3 = 12 + 4 - 3 = 13$

When $x = -2$, $\dfrac{d^2y}{dx^2} = 6 \times (-2) - 2 = -12 - 2 = -14$

In Example 3, notice that the gradient is positive but the second derivative is negative. This means that the rate of change of the gradient is negative, so the graph is increasing less rapidly.

Using the second derivative to determine the nature of stationary points

At a stationary point, the sign of the second derivative can often tell you the nature of the stationary point.

When $\dfrac{dy}{dx} = 0$, there is a stationary point.

- If $\dfrac{d^2y}{dx^2} < 0$, it is a local maximum.

- If $\dfrac{d^2y}{dx^2} > 0$, it is a local minimum.

- If $\dfrac{d^2y}{dx^2} = 0$, check the gradient either side of the stationary point.

EXAMPLE 4

The curve $y = 2x^5 + 5x^4 - 1$ has stationary points at $(-2, 15)$ and $(0, -1)$.

Determine the nature of these stationary points.

SOLUTION

$y = 2x^5 + 5x^4 - 1 \Rightarrow \dfrac{dy}{dx} = 10x^4 + 20x^3 \Rightarrow \dfrac{d^2y}{dx^2} = 40x^3 + 60x^2$

When $x = -2$, $\dfrac{d^2y}{dx^2} = 40(-2)^3 + 60(-2)^2 = -320 + 240 = -80$

Since the second derivative is negative, $(-2, 15)$ is a local maximum point.

When $x = 0$, $\dfrac{d^2y}{dx^2} = 40 \times 0^3 + 60 \times 0^2 = 0$

Since the second derivative is zero, test the gradient function on either side.

When $x = -1$, $\dfrac{dy}{dx} = 10(-1)^4 + 20(-1)^3 = 10 - 20 = -10$

When $x = 1$, $\dfrac{dy}{dx} = 10 \times 1^4 + 20 \times 1^3 = 10 + 20 = 30$

The gradient function is going from negative to positive, so $(0, -1)$ is a local minimum point.

LINKS

This work has applications throughout Pure Mathematics and Mechanics.

Test Yourself ▷L

1 Look at the three functions below.

$$f(x) = x^3 \qquad g(x) = x^3 + x \qquad h(x) = x^2 + x$$

Which of these functions are increasing functions of x for all values of x?

A f only   B f and g   C g only   D f and h   E h only

2 Find the range of values of x for which the function $y = x^3 + 2x^2 + x + 2$ is a decreasing function of x.

A $x < -1$ and $x > -\frac{1}{3}$ B $x \leqslant -1$ and $x \geqslant -\frac{1}{3}$ C $x < -2$

D $-1 \leqslant x \leqslant -\frac{1}{3}$ E $-1 < x < -\frac{1}{3}$

3 Find the value of the second derivative of the curve $y = x^4 - 3x^2 - x + 1$ at the point where $x = -2$.

A -21 B 42   C -54 D 10   E -18

4 Find the value of the second derivative of the curve $y = \dfrac{1}{3x}$ at the point where $x = 3$.

A $\frac{2}{81}$ B $-\frac{2}{81}$ C $\frac{2}{9}$ D $-\frac{1}{27}$ E $-\frac{2}{9}$

5 Find the y co-ordinate of the point on the curve $y = x^3 + 6x^2 + 5x - 3$ at which the second derivative is zero.

A -2 B -45 C 3   D -7 E 9

Exam-Style Question ▷L

A curve has equation $y = x^3 - 3x^2 - 9x + 2$.

i) Find $\dfrac{dy}{dx}$ and $\dfrac{d^2y}{dx^2}$.

ii) Find the range of values of x for which y is an increasing function of x.

iii) The curve has a stationary point at $(-1, 7)$. Use the second derivative to find the nature of this stationary point.

Integration

Indefinite integration

▶▶ 234
347

A ABOUT THIS TOPIC

Integration is the opposite process to differentiation. You can use integration to find the equation of a curve if you know its derivative, $\dfrac{dy}{dx}$, and a point that it passes through.

R REMEMBER

- Differentiation from C2.
- Substituting the co-ordinates of a point into the equation of curve from C2.

K KEY FACTS

- The *rule* for integrating a power of x is:

$$\int ax^n dx = \frac{ax^{n+1}}{n+1} + c$$

- The rule is often expressed in words as: 'Increase the power by 1 and divide by the new power'.

- The '$+ c$' is known as the **constant of integration**.

- If you know a derivative, $\dfrac{dy}{dx}$, you can find the equation of the curve by integrating, but remember the constant of integration.

- To find a particular solution through a point substitute the co-ordinates into the equation to find the value of the constant of integration.

Basic indefinite integration

The *rule* for integrating a power of x is:

$$\int ax^n dx = \frac{ax^{n+1}}{n+1} + c$$

This is the reverse of the rule for differentiating:

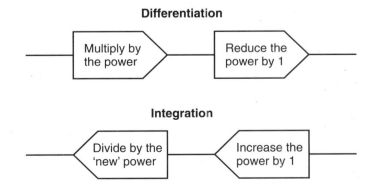

Differentiation

Multiply by the power | Reduce the power by 1

Integration

Divide by the 'new' power | Increase the power by 1

EXAMPLE 1

Find the following:

i) $\int 12x^2 dx$

ii) $\int 5x dx$

iii) $\int (3x^2 + 10x - 1) dx$

iv) $\int 3 dx$

SOLUTION

i) $\int 12x^2 dx = \dfrac{12x^3}{3} + c$ ← *Increase the power by 1 and divide by the new power.*

$= 4x^3 + c$ ← *Don't forget the '+ c'.*

ii) $\int 5x dx = \dfrac{5x^2}{2} + c$

iii) $\int (3x^2 + 10x - 1) dx = \dfrac{3x^3}{3} + \dfrac{10x^2}{2} - x + c$ ← *Integrate each term separately and then add them (the same as you'd do for differentiation).*

$= x^3 + 5x^2 - x + c$

iv) $\int 3 dx = 3x + c$

⚠️ Do not get confused integrating a constant term, or number. You can think of this in two ways:

- $3x$ differentiates to 3, so 3 integrates to $3x$ (because integration is the opposite of differentiation)
- 3 can be written as $3x^0$ which would integrate to $\dfrac{3x^1}{1}$ or $3x$.

Reversing differentiation

If you know a derivative, $\dfrac{dy}{dx}$, you can find the equation of the curve by integrating.

To find a particular solution through a point, substitute the co-ordinates into the equation to find the value of the constant of integration.

EXAMPLE 2

The gradient function of a curve is $\dfrac{dy}{dx} = 2x$. The curve passes through $(2, 7)$. Find the equation of the curve.

SOLUTION

Integrating $\dfrac{dy}{dx} = 2x$ gives $y = \dfrac{2x^2}{2} + c$ which simplifies to $y = x^2 + c$.

Substitute the point $(2, 7)$ in to the equation:
$7 = 2^2 + c$
$7 = 4 + c$
$c = 3$

So the equation of the curve is $y = x^2 + 3$.

EXAMPLE 3

A curve passes through $(-1, 8)$ and its gradient is given by $\dfrac{dy}{dx} = 3x^2 + 6x - 9$. Find the equation of the curve and sketch the graph of y against x showing the co-ordinates of the intercept with the y axis and any stationary points.

SOLUTION

Integrating gives $y = \dfrac{3x^3}{3} + \dfrac{6x^2}{2} - 9x + c$ which simplifies to $y = x^3 + 3x^2 - 9x + c$.

Substitute the point $(-1, 8)$ in to the equation:

$$8 = (-1)^3 + 3 \times (-1)^2 - 9 \times (-1) + c$$
$$8 = -1 + 3 + 9 + c$$
$$c = -3$$

So the equation of the curve is $y = x^3 + 3x^2 - 9x - 3$

The graph intercepts the y axis at $y = -3$.

The stationary points on the curve are where $\dfrac{dy}{dx} = 0$,

$$3x^2 + 6x - 9 = 0$$
$$\Rightarrow 3(x^2 + 2x - 3) = 0$$
$$\Rightarrow 3(x + 3)(x - 1) = 0$$
$$\Rightarrow x = -3 \text{ or } x = 1$$

Substituting these into the equation of the curve gives:

$$y = (-3)^3 + 3 \times (-3)^2 - 9 \times (-3) - 3$$
$$= 24$$
$$y = 1^3 + 3 \times 1^2 - 9 \times 1 - 3$$
$$= -8$$

(Graph labelled with points $(-3, 24)$, $(1, -8)$, and intercept at -3 on the x axis.)

LINKS

Pure Mathematics	Core 3, Core 4, Further Pure 2, Further Pure 3, Differential Equations, Numerical Methods.
Mechanics	Mechanics 1–4.
Statistics	Statistics 3, Statistics 4.

Test Yourself ▶L

1 Find $\int 2x^3 \mathrm{d}x$.

  A $\dfrac{2x^3}{3} + c$ B $\dfrac{x^4}{2} + c$ C $6x^2 + c$ D $\dfrac{2x^4}{3} + c$

2 Find $\int (3x^2 + 1)\mathrm{d}x$.

  A $x^3 + c$ B $6x + c$ C $x^3 + 1 + c$ D $x^3 + x + c$

3 A curve has gradient given by $\dfrac{\mathrm{d}y}{\mathrm{d}x} = 4x$ and passes through the point $(-2, 3)$.
What is the equation of the curve?

  A $y = 4x + 11$ B $y = 2x^2 + 11$ C $y = 2x^2 - 20$ D $y = 2x^2 - 5$

4 A curve has gradient given by $\dfrac{\mathrm{d}y}{\mathrm{d}x} = 6x^2 - 6x$ and passes through the point $(2, -1)$.
What is the equation of the curve?

  A $y = 2x^3 - 3x^2 - 5$ B $y = 12x - 6$ C $y = 6x^3 - 6x^2 - 23$ D $y = 2x^3 - 3x^2 + 7$

5 A curve has gradient given by $\dfrac{\mathrm{d}y}{\mathrm{d}x} = x^2 - 2x + 1$ and passes through the point $(-1, -2)$.
Where does the curve intercept the y-axis?

  A $y = -1\frac{2}{3}$ B $y = -2$ C $y = -1$ D $y = \frac{1}{3}$

Exam-Style Question ▶L

a) Find $\int (6x^2 + 5x - 3)\mathrm{d}x$.

b) A curve has gradient given by $\dfrac{\mathrm{d}y}{\mathrm{d}x} = 3x^2 - 2$. The curve passes through the point $(-2, 1)$.
Find the equation of the curve.

Finding areas by integration

A | ABOUT THIS TOPIC

Areas bounded by curves may be found exactly by integration if you can integrate the boundary curve.

R | REMEMBER

- Area work from GCSE.
- Integrating a function from C1.

K | KEY FACTS

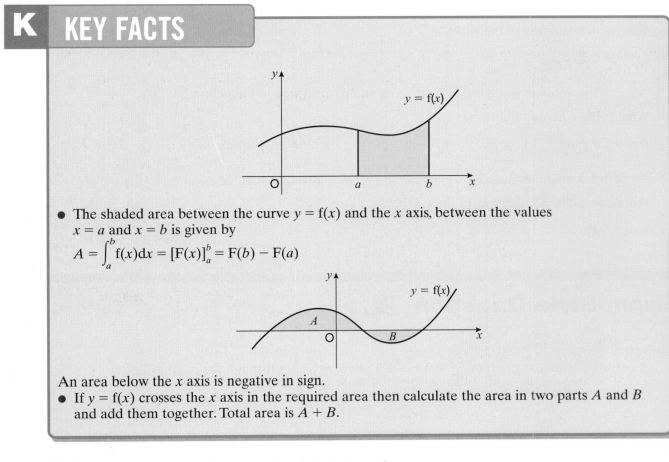

- The shaded area between the curve $y = f(x)$ and the x axis, between the values $x = a$ and $x = b$ is given by

$$A = \int_a^b f(x)dx = [F(x)]_a^b = F(b) - F(a)$$

An area below the x axis is negative in sign.
- If $y = f(x)$ crosses the x axis in the required area then calculate the area in two parts A and B and add them together. Total area is $A + B$.

Finding an area requires the use of definite integration.

EXAMPLE 1

Evaluate the definite integral $\int_1^3 (x^4 + 4x^3 - 3x^2)dx$.

SOLUTION

$$\int_1^3 (x^4 + 4x^3 - 3x^2)dx = \left[\frac{x^5}{5} + \frac{4x^4}{4} - \frac{3x^3}{3}\right]_1^3$$

Remember $\int x^n = \frac{x^{n+1}}{n+1} + C$. Increase the index, n, by 1, and then divide by the new index.

$$= \left[\frac{x^5}{5} + x^4 - x^3\right]_1^3$$

$$= \left(\frac{3^5}{5} + 3^4 - 3^3\right) - \left(\frac{1}{5} + 1 - 1\right) = \frac{243}{5} + 81 - 27 - \frac{1}{5}$$

$$= \frac{242}{5} + 54 = \frac{512}{5} = 102\tfrac{2}{5}$$

This forms part of the working for an area problem.

If you are asked for an exact answer, do not use the 'numerical integration' function on your calculator. An exact answer may be an integer, or contain a fraction, a surd, or a number such as π.
$\sqrt{3}$ is exact; 1.732 is not.
$\frac{29}{7}$ is exact; 4.143 is not.

The area between a curve and the x axis

EXAMPLE 2

i) Draw the graph of $y = (x + 1)(2 - x)$.
ii) Find the area bounded by the curve $y = (x + 1)(2 - x)$ and the x axis.

SOLUTION

This curve crosses the x axis at $x = -1$ and at $x = 2$ and the y axis at 2.

i)

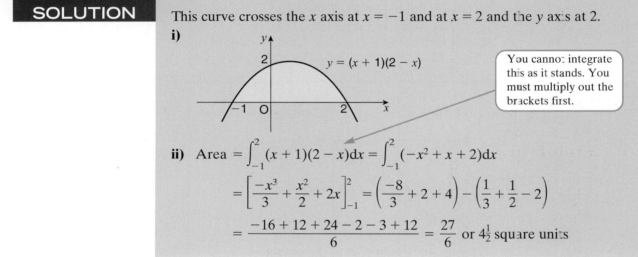

$y = (x + 1)(2 - x)$

You cannot integrate this as it stands. You must multiply out the brackets first.

ii) Area $= \displaystyle\int_{-1}^{2} (x + 1)(2 - x)\,dx = \int_{-1}^{2} (-x^2 + x + 2)\,dx$

$= \left[\dfrac{-x^3}{3} + \dfrac{x^2}{2} + 2x \right]_{-1}^{2} = \left(\dfrac{-8}{3} + 2 + 4 \right) - \left(\dfrac{1}{3} + \dfrac{1}{2} - 2 \right)$

$= \dfrac{-16 + 12 + 24 - 2 - 3 + 12}{6} = \dfrac{27}{6}$ or $4\frac{1}{2}$ square units

Areas below the x axis

If an area is below the x axis it has a negative sign. A curve may cross the x axis within the area required. In this case evaluate the area above the axis and the area below the axis separately and then add them.

A ADVICE

Always sketch the curve to check whether it crosses the axis.

EXAMPLE 3

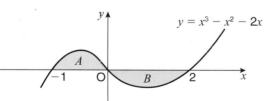

$y = x^3 - x^2 - 2x$

The graph shows the curve $y = x^3 - x^2 - 2x$.
i) Find the area of the shaded region.
ii) Evaluate $\displaystyle\int_{-1}^{2} (x^3 - x^2 - 2x)\,dx$.
iii) Explain why your answers to parts **i)** and **ii)** are not the same.

SOLUTION

i) $A = \int_{-1}^{0} (x^3 - x^2 - 2x)dx = \left[\dfrac{x^4}{4} - \dfrac{x^3}{3} - \dfrac{2x^2}{2}\right]_{-1}^{0} = (0) - \left(\dfrac{1}{4} + \dfrac{1}{3} - 1\right) = \dfrac{5}{12}$

$B = \int_{0}^{2} (x^3 - x^2 - 2x)dx = \left[\dfrac{x^4}{4} - \dfrac{x^3}{3} - \dfrac{2x^2}{2}\right]_{0}^{2} = \left(\dfrac{16}{4} - \dfrac{8}{3} - 4\right) - (0) = -\dfrac{8}{3}$

> This area is negative because it is below the x axis.

Total shaded area $= A + B = \dfrac{5}{12} + \dfrac{8}{3} = \dfrac{37}{12}$ or $3\dfrac{1}{12}$ or square units.

ii) $\int_{-1}^{2} (x^3 - x^2 - 2x)dx = \left[\dfrac{x^4}{4} - \dfrac{x^3}{3} - \dfrac{2x^2}{2}\right]_{-1}^{2} = \left(\dfrac{16}{4} - \dfrac{8}{3} - 4\right) - \left(\dfrac{1}{4} + \dfrac{1}{3} - 1\right)$

$= -\dfrac{8}{3} + \dfrac{5}{12} = \dfrac{-27}{12}$ or $-2\dfrac{1}{4}$

> The answer to part ii) is the net area above the x axis.

iii) The answers to parts i) and ii) are different because in part i) the fractions are added without regard to sign but in part ii) the minus sign means that the fractions were subtracted.

EXAMPLE 4

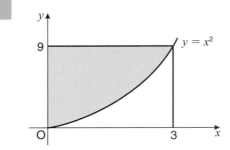

The graph shows part of the curve $y = x^2$.

i) Find the area between the curve and the x axis for $0 \leqslant x \leqslant 3$.

ii) Hence find the area of the shaded region.

SOLUTION

i) Area $= \int_{0}^{3} x^2 dx = \left[\dfrac{x^3}{3}\right]_{0}^{3} = \dfrac{27}{3} - 0 = 9$ square units.

ii) Shaded area $= 9 \times 3 - 9 = 27 - 9 = 18$ square units.

A ADVICE

An alternative way of answering this question is to use the formula $\int x\,dy$ for the area between the curve and the y axis.

Area $= \int x\,dy = \int_{0}^{9} y^{\frac{1}{2}}\,dy = \left[\dfrac{y^{\frac{3}{2}}}{\frac{3}{2}}\right]_{0}^{9} = \left(\dfrac{2 \times 9^{\frac{3}{2}}}{3}\right) - (0) = \dfrac{2 \times 27}{3} = 18$ square units.

LINKS

Pure Mathematics	Integration, Areas 2.
Mechanics	Centres of Mass (M3), Moments of Inertia (M4).
Statistics	Probability Density Functions (S3).

Test Yourself ▶L

1 Here is the graph of $y = 4 - x^2$.

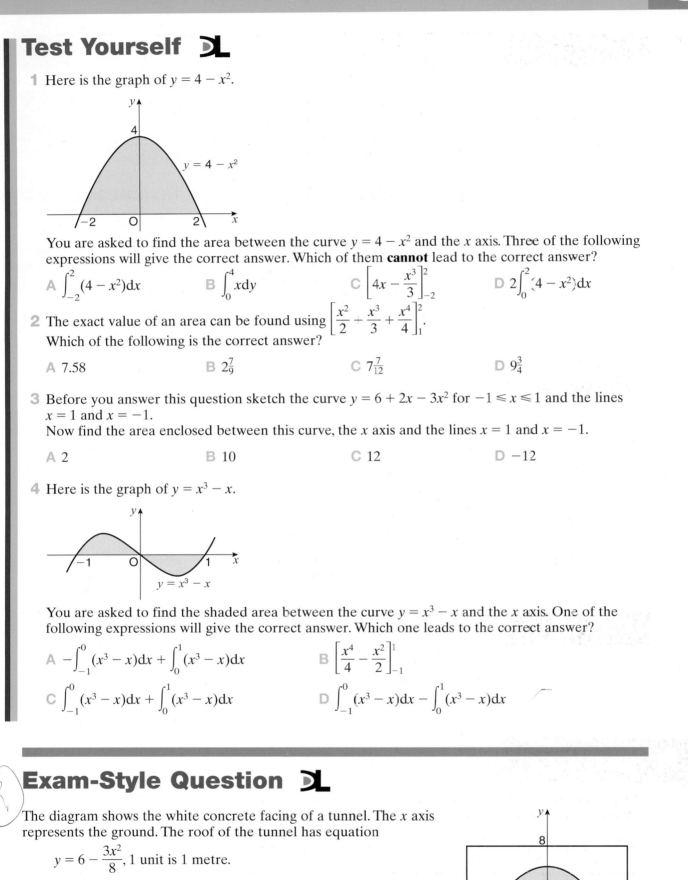

You are asked to find the area between the curve $y = 4 - x^2$ and the x axis. Three of the following expressions will give the correct answer. Which of them **cannot** lead to the correct answer?

A $\int_{-2}^{2} (4 - x^2)dx$

B $\int_{0}^{4} x\,dy$

C $\left[4x - \dfrac{x^3}{3} \right]_{-2}^{2}$

D $2\int_{0}^{2} (4 - x^2)dx$

2 The exact value of an area can be found using $\left[\dfrac{x^2}{2} + \dfrac{x^3}{3} + \dfrac{x^4}{4} \right]_{1}^{2}$.
Which of the following is the correct answer?

A 7.58

B $2\frac{7}{9}$

C $7\frac{7}{12}$

D $9\frac{3}{4}$

3 Before you answer this question sketch the curve $y = 6 + 2x - 3x^2$ for $-1 \leqslant x \leqslant 1$ and the lines $x = 1$ and $x = -1$.
Now find the area enclosed between this curve, the x axis and the lines $x = 1$ and $x = -1$.

A 2

B 10

C 12

D −12

4 Here is the graph of $y = x^3 - x$.

You are asked to find the shaded area between the curve $y = x^3 - x$ and the x axis. One of the following expressions will give the correct answer. Which one leads to the correct answer?

A $-\int_{-1}^{0} (x^3 - x)dx + \int_{0}^{1} (x^3 - x)dx$

B $\left[\dfrac{x^4}{4} - \dfrac{x^2}{2} \right]_{-1}^{1}$

C $\int_{-1}^{0} (x^3 - x)dx + \int_{0}^{1} (x^3 - x)dx$

D $\int_{-1}^{0} (x^3 - x)dx - \int_{0}^{1} (x^3 - x)dx$

Exam-Style Question ▶L

The diagram shows the white concrete facing of a tunnel. The x axis represents the ground. The roof of the tunnel has equation

$$y = 6 - \frac{3x^2}{8}, \text{ 1 unit is 1 metre.}$$

i) Find the co-ordinates of A and B.

ii) Find the area between the curve and the x axis.

iii) Calculate the cost of repainting the facing at £5 per square metre.

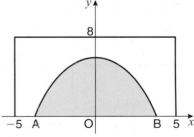

Further areas

K | **KEY FACTS**

- Areas between curves
  Areas not bounded by the x axis or the y axis can be found by addition or subtraction of simpler areas.

- Trapezium rule
  The area between the curve $y = f(x)$ and the x axis, between the values $y = a$ and $y = b$ can be estimated by using the trapezium rule

  $$A = \frac{h}{2}[y_0 + y_n + 2(y_1 + y_2 + \ldots y_{n-1})]$$

  where the area is divided into n strips each of width h.

- A sketch of the curve will show whether the trapezium rule gives an underestimate or an overestimate of the actual area.

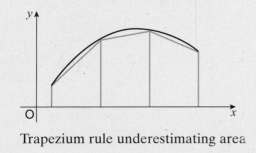

Trapezium rule underestimating area

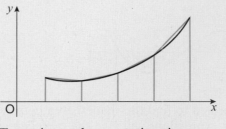

Trapezium rule overestimating area

The area between two curves

EXAMPLE 1

i) Sketch the curves $y = 5 + 4x - x^2$ and $y = x^2 - 4x + 5$.

ii) Show that the curves cross when $x = 0$ and 4.

iii) Find the area between $y = 5 + 4x - x^2$, the x axis and the lines $x = 0$ and $x = 4$.

iv) Find the area between $y = x^2 - 4x + 5$, the x axis and the lines $x = 0$ and $x = 4$.

v) Hence find the area between the two curves.

i)

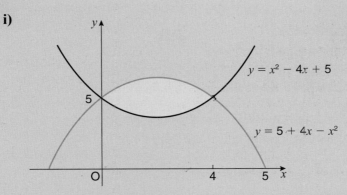

ii) These curves intersect where the x and y values are the same on both curves.

Hence $x^2 - 4x + 5 = 5 + 4x - x^2 \Rightarrow 2x^2 - 8x = 0$

so $\qquad\qquad 2x(x - 4) = 0 \Rightarrow x = 0$ or $x = 4$

> The co-ordinates of the points of intersection are $(0, 5)$ and $(4, 5)$.

iii) The area between $y = 5 + 4x - x^2$, the x axis, $x = 0$ and $x = 4$ is given by

$$\int_0^4 (5 + 4x - x^2)\mathrm{d}x = \left[5x + \frac{4x^2}{2} - \frac{x^3}{3} \right]_0^4$$

$$= \left(20 + 32 - \tfrac{64}{3} \right) - (0)$$

$$= 30\tfrac{2}{3}$$

iv) The area between $y = x^2 - 4x + 5$, the x axis, $x = 0$ and $x = 4$ is given by

$$\int_0^4 (x^2 - 4x + 5)\mathrm{d}x = \left[\frac{x^3}{3} - \frac{4x^2}{2} + 5x \right]_0^4$$

$$= \left(\tfrac{64}{3} - 32 + 20 \right) - (0)$$

$$= 9\tfrac{1}{3}$$

v) Hence the area between the two curves is $30\tfrac{2}{3} - 9\tfrac{1}{3} = 21\tfrac{1}{3}$ square units.

An alternative method for finding the area between the curves is to integrate the difference between the curves.

$$A = \int (\text{top curve} - \text{bottom curve})\mathrm{d}x$$

In this case $\quad$ Area $= \int_0^4 [(5 + 4x - x^2) - (x^2 - 4x + 5)]\mathrm{d}x$

$$= \int_0^4 (8x - 2x^2)\mathrm{d}x$$

$$= \left[\frac{8x^2}{2} - \frac{2x^3}{3} \right]_0^4$$

$$= \left(64 - \frac{128}{3} \right) - (0)$$

$$= 21\tfrac{1}{3} \text{ square units}$$

Top curve
$y = 5 + 4x - x^2$

Bottom curve
$y = x^2 - 4x + 5$

A ADVICE

This alternative method, using $\int(\text{top curve} - \text{bottom curve})$, means that you do not have to worry about where the curves cross the x axis. So to find the shaded area in the diagram,

all you need is $\int_{-3}^{3}[(x^2) - (2x^2 - 9)]dx$.

Check it for yourself. The answer is 36 square units.

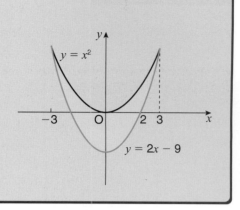

Using the trapezium rule

Sometimes you need to find the area under a curve but don't know the equation of the function or it is one you cannot integrate. In these cases you can use a numerical method, for example, the trapezium rule. The formula for this is

$$A = \frac{h}{2}[y_0 + y_n + 2(y_1 + y_2 + \ldots y_{n+1})].$$

You can see how to use it in the next two examples.

EXAMPLE 2

This table gives the values of y for different values of x.

x	1	3	5	7	9
y	45	34	25	18	11

These could be the results from an experiment or they could be measurements, for example.

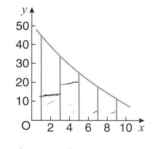

Use the trapezium rule to find an approximate value of $\int_{1}^{9} y\,dx$.

SOLUTION

$$A = \frac{h}{2}[y_0 + y_n + 2(y_1 + y_2 + \ldots y_{n-1})]$$

where $h = 2$ and the y values are given in the table.

$$A = \frac{1}{2} \times 2[45 + 11 + 2(34 + 25 + 18)] = 210 \text{ square units}$$

3

EXAMPLE 3

Use the trapezium rule with 4 intervals to evaluate $\int_{-1}^{1} \sqrt{(x+1)}\,dx$ stating whether your answer is an underestimate or an overestimate.

SOLUTION

This time $h = \frac{1}{2}$, $n = 4$ and there are 5 values.

> You will need your calculator to work out some of the y values.

x	$y = \sqrt{x+1}$		
-1	0		0
-0.5	0.7071	×2	1.4142 …
0	1	×2	2
0.5	1.225	×2	2.45
1	1.4142		1.4142 …
		Total	7.2784 …

> y_0 and y_4

> $2y_1$, $2y_2$ and $2y_3$

Hence $A = \frac{1}{4}[7.2784 \ldots] = 1.8196 \ldots = 1.82$ square units to 2 d.p.

Here is a sketch of the curve $y = \sqrt{(x+1)}$.

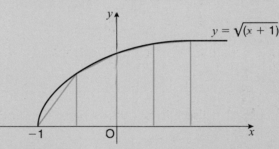

$$y = \sqrt{(x+1)}$$

The curve is above the lines forming the trapezia so this approximation is an underestimate.

LINKS

Pure Mathematics	Integration (C3).
Mechanics	Centres of Mass (M3), Moments of Inertia (M4).
Statistics	Probability Density Functions (S3).

Test Yourself ▶L

1 Here is a sketch of the curves $y = x^2 - 2x$ (black) and $y = x^3 + 3x^2 - 5x$ (orange) which intersect at P, Q and R. You are required to find the area between the curves, point **P** and point Q. The working is given below but there is a mistake in it. At which line does the mistake occur?

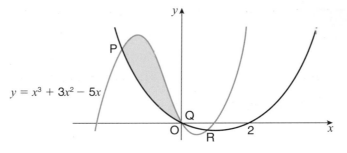

A At points of intersection $x^3 + 3x^2 - 5x = x^2 - 2x$
$$x^3 + 2x^2 - 3x = 0$$

B $x(x + 3)(x - 1) = 0$

C so P is $(-3, 3)$, Q is $(0, 0)$, and R is $(1, -1)$

D Area $\int_{-3}^{0} (x^3 + 3x^2 - 5x)dx - \int_{-3}^{0} (x^2 - 2x)dx$

$$= \int_{-3}^{0} (x^3 + 2x^2 - 3x)dx$$

$$= \left[\frac{x^4}{4} + \frac{2x^3}{3} - \frac{3x^2}{2} \right]_{-3}^{0}$$

E $$= 0 - \left[\frac{81}{4} - 18 - \frac{27}{2} \right] = -11\tfrac{1}{4}$$

2 Here is a sketch of the curves $y = x^5$ (orange) and $y = x^6$ (black) which intersect at $(0, 0)$ and $(1, 1)$. Find the area enclosed between the curves.

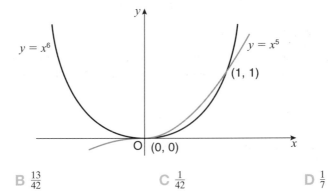

A $\frac{1}{6}$ B $\frac{13}{42}$ C $\frac{1}{42}$ D $\frac{1}{7}$

3 It is required to estimate the area between the x axis and the curve $y = f(x)$ between $x = 0$ and $x = 12$. This is done by using the trapezium rule on a given number of strips. Which of the following is a correct application of the trapezium rule?

A 2 strips: $A = \frac{6}{2}[y_0 + y_1 + y_2]$

B 3 strips: $A = \frac{4}{2}[y_0 + 2(y_1 + y_2)]$

C 4 strips: $A = 3[y_0 + y_4 + 2(y_1 + y_2 + y_3)]$

D 5 strips: $A = \frac{12}{10}[y_0 + 2(y_1 + y_2 + y_3 + y_4) + y_5]$

E 6 strips: $A = \frac{12}{12}[y_0 + y_6 + 2(y_1 + y_2 + y_3 + y_4)]$

4 A curve passes through the points given in this table.

x	1	4	7
y	0	12	42

Use the trapezium rule to estimate the area between the curve and the x axis.

A 198   B 81   C 162   D 99

Exam-Style Question ▶L

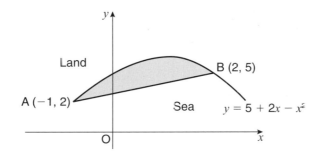

The diagram is a map of a length of coastline. It can be modelled by the curve $y = 5 + 2x - x^2$. Units are kilometres. It is planned to build a wall from A $(-1, 2)$ to B $(2, 5)$. The shaded region, between the wall and the coast, will become reclaimed land.

i)   Verify that the equation of the retaining wall is $y = x + 3$.

ii)   Find the area between the curve $y = 5 + 2x - x^2$, the x axis and the lines $x = -1$ and $x = 2$.

iii) Find the area between the line $y = x + 3$, the x axis and the lines $x = -1$ and $x = 2$.

iv)   Calculate the area of land to be reclaimed.

v)   Simplify and evaluate $\int_{-1}^{2} [(5 + 2x - x^2) - (x + 3)]dx$.

vi)   Comment on your answers to parts iv) and v).

vii) A new map of the area is issued, showing that part of the coastline has been eroded. Use the trapezium rule and the following points taken from the map to estimate the new area that will now be reclaimed.

x	−1	−0.5	0	0.5	1	1.5	2
y	2	4.3	5.2	5.9	6.2	5.8	5

Further integration

You have already seen how the rule for differentiating positive whole number powers can be extended to negative and fractional powers. You can extend the rule for integrating in the same way.

- Differentiation from C2.
- Basic integration from C2.
- Laws of indices from C1.
- Substituting a pair of co-ordinates into the equation of curve from C1, C2.

- The *rule* for integrating a power of x:

$$\int ax^n \mathrm{d}x = \frac{ax^{n+1}}{n+1} + c$$

can be used when n is a fraction or a negative number (except for -1).

EXAMPLE 1

Find

i) $\int \frac{8}{x^3} \mathrm{d}x$

ii) $\int 3\sqrt{x} \mathrm{d}x$

iii) $\int \left(x^2 + \frac{1}{x^2} \right) \mathrm{d}x$

iv) $\int \frac{\sqrt{x}}{x} \mathrm{d}x$

SOLUTION

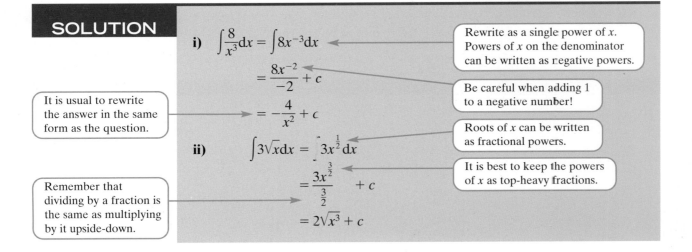

i) $\int \frac{8}{x^3} \mathrm{d}x = \int 8x^{-3} \mathrm{d}x$ ← Rewrite as a single power of x. Powers of x on the denominator can be written as negative powers.

$= \frac{8x^{-2}}{-2} + c$ ← Be careful when adding 1 to a negative number!

It is usual to rewrite the answer in the same form as the question. → $= -\frac{4}{x^2} + c$

Roots of x can be written as fractional powers.

ii) $\int 3\sqrt{x} \mathrm{d}x = \int 3x^{\frac{1}{2}} \mathrm{d}x$

It is best to keep the powers of x as top-heavy fractions.

$= \frac{3x^{\frac{3}{2}}}{\frac{3}{2}} + c$

Remember that dividing by a fraction is the same as multiplying by it upside-down. → $= 2\sqrt{x^3} + c$

SOLUTION

iii) $\int \left(x^2 + \dfrac{1}{x^2}\right)dx = \int (x^2 + x^{-2})dx$ ← Integrate each term separately, just like you'd normally do with sums of powers of x.

$= \dfrac{x^3}{3} + \dfrac{x^{-1}}{-1} + c$

$= \dfrac{x^3}{3} - \dfrac{1}{x} + c$

iv) $\int \dfrac{\sqrt{x}}{x}dx = \int \dfrac{x^{\frac{1}{2}}}{x^1}dx$ ← Remember the laws of indices When dividing powers subtract the indices

$= \int x^{-\frac{1}{2}}dx$

$= \dfrac{x^{\frac{1}{2}}}{\frac{1}{2}} + c$

$= 2\sqrt{x} + c$ ← Don't forget the '+ c'.

EXAMPLE 2

i) Find $\displaystyle\int_2^5 \dfrac{3}{x^2}dx$

ii) Find $\displaystyle\int_1^3 \sqrt[3]{x}\,dx$

SOLUTION

i) $\displaystyle\int_2^5 \dfrac{3}{x^2}dx = \int_2^5 3x^{-2}dx$

$= \left[\dfrac{3x^{-1}}{-1}\right]_2^5$ ← You might find it easier to rewrite x^{-1} as $\dfrac{1}{x}$ to help you when evaluating it at 5 and 2.

$= \left[-\dfrac{3}{x}\right]_2^5$

$= \left[-\dfrac{3}{5}\right] - \left[-\dfrac{3}{2}\right]$

$= \dfrac{9}{10}$

ii) $\displaystyle\int_1^8 \sqrt[3]{x}\,dx = \int_1^8 x^{\frac{1}{3}}dx$

$= \left[\dfrac{x^{\frac{4}{3}}}{\frac{4}{3}}\right]_1^8$ ← Remember what fractional indices mean. $x^{\frac{4}{3}}$ is the same as $(\sqrt[3]{x})^4$. You can also write it as $\sqrt[3]{x^4}$ but it is often easier to work out the numbers in the form used here.

$= \left[\dfrac{3}{4}(\sqrt[3]{x})^4\right]_1^8$

$= \left[\dfrac{3}{4}(\sqrt[3]{8})^4\right] - \left[\dfrac{3}{4}(\sqrt[3]{1})^4\right]$

$= \left[\dfrac{3}{4} \times 16\right] - \left[\dfrac{3}{4} \times 1\right]$

$= 12 - \dfrac{3}{4}$

$= 11\dfrac{1}{4}$

EXAMPLE 3

The graph of $y = x^2 + \dfrac{1}{x^3}$ is shown.

The shaded region is bounded by the curve, the x axis and the lines $x = 1$ and $x = 3$.
Find the area of the shaded region.

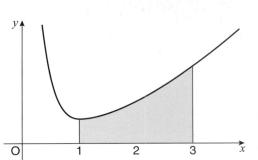

SOLUTION

$$\int_1^3 \left(x^2 + \frac{1}{x^3}\right) dx = \int_1^3 (x^2 + x^{-3}) dx$$

To find an area integrate the function between the two limits.

$$= \left[\frac{x^3}{3} + \frac{x^{-2}}{-2}\right]_1^3$$

Be careful when adding 1 to a negative number!

$$= \left[\frac{x^3}{3} - \frac{1}{2x^2}\right]_1^3$$

Rewriting should help you find the values at $x = 3$ and 1.

$$= \left[\frac{3^3}{3} - \frac{1}{2 \times 3^2}\right] - \left[\frac{1^3}{3} - \frac{1}{2 \times 1^2}\right]$$

$$= 8\tfrac{17}{18} - \left(-\tfrac{1}{6}\right)$$

$$= 9\tfrac{1}{9}$$

EXAMPLE 4

The gradient of a curve is given by $\dfrac{dy}{dx} = \dfrac{5}{x^4}$. The curve passes through $(1, 2)$.
Find the equation of the curve.

SOLUTION

$\dfrac{dy}{dx} = \dfrac{5}{x^4}$ can be rewritten as $\dfrac{dy}{dx} = 5x^{-4}$

If you know $\dfrac{dy}{dx}$ then integrating will give you y.

$$y = \int 5x^{-4} dx$$

$$y = \frac{5x^{-3}}{-3} + c$$

Use the co-ordinates of the point you have been given to find the value of c.

$$y = -\frac{5}{3x^3} + c$$

Substitute $x = 1$ and $y = 2$ into the equation: $2 = -\dfrac{5}{3 \times 1^3} + c$, so $c = 3\tfrac{2}{3}$.

So the equation of the curve is $y = 3\tfrac{2}{3} - \dfrac{5}{3x^3}$.

LINKS

Pure Mathematics	Integration (C3, C4), Calculus (FP2), Differential Geometry (FP3), Differential Equations (DE), Numerical Methods.
Mechanics	Volumes of Revolution and Centres of Mass (M3), Variable Force and Mass (M4).
Statistics	Probability Density Functions (S3).

Test Yourself ▷L

1 Find $\int \dfrac{3}{x^2}dx$.

   A $3x^{-2} + c$ B $-\dfrac{6}{x^3} + c$ C $-\dfrac{3}{x} + c$ D $2x^{\frac{3}{2}} + c$

2 Find $\int \sqrt[3]{x}\,dx$.

   A $-\dfrac{1}{2x^2} + c$ B $x^{\frac{1}{3}} + c$ C $\dfrac{1}{3\sqrt[3]{x^2}} + c$ D $\dfrac{3(\sqrt[3]{x})^4}{4} + c$

3 Find $\int_{1}^{4} \sqrt{x}\,dx$.

   A $\frac{21}{2}$ B $\frac{3}{4}$ C 1 D $\frac{14}{3}$

4 Find $\int_{2}^{4} \left(x^3 + \dfrac{1}{x^3} \right)dx$.

   A $56\frac{9}{64}$ B $60\frac{3}{32}$ C $60\frac{15}{1024}$ D $59\frac{29}{32}$

5 The gradient of a curve is given by $\dfrac{dy}{dx} = \dfrac{3}{x^4}$. The curve passes through $(1, 2)$. Find the equation of the curve.

   A $y = 3 - \dfrac{1}{x^3}$ B $y = -\dfrac{12}{x^5}$ C $y = 1\frac{1}{8} - \dfrac{1}{x^3}$ D $y = 2\frac{3}{5} - \dfrac{3}{5x^5}$

Exam-Style Question ▷L

a) Find $\int \left(3\sqrt{x} + \dfrac{1}{x^2} \right)dx$.

b) A curve has gradient given by $\dfrac{dy}{dx} = \dfrac{2}{x^2}$. The curve passes through the point $(3, 1)$.
Find the equation of the curve.

Trigonometry

Basic trigonometry

K **KEY FACTS**

- Trigonometrical functions for values of angle θ between $0°$ and $90°$ inclusive.

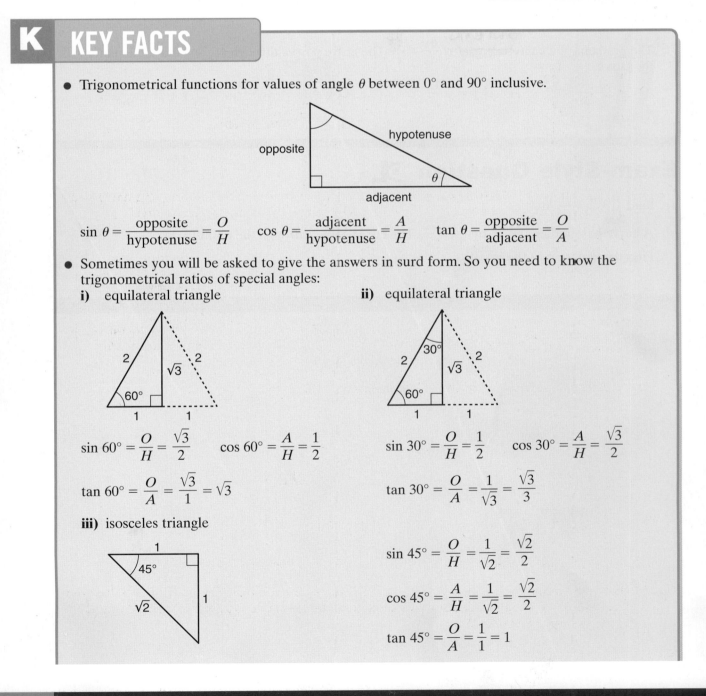

$$\sin \theta = \frac{\text{opposite}}{\text{hypotenuse}} = \frac{O}{H} \qquad \cos \theta = \frac{\text{adjacent}}{\text{hypotenuse}} = \frac{A}{H} \qquad \tan \theta = \frac{\text{opposite}}{\text{adjacent}} = \frac{O}{A}$$

- Sometimes you will be asked to give the answers in surd form. So you need to know the trigonometrical ratios of special angles:

  i) equilateral triangle

  $$\sin 60° = \frac{O}{H} = \frac{\sqrt{3}}{2} \qquad \cos 60° = \frac{A}{H} = \frac{1}{2}$$

  $$\tan 60° = \frac{O}{A} = \frac{\sqrt{3}}{1} = \sqrt{3}$$

  ii) equilateral triangle

  $$\sin 30° = \frac{O}{H} = \frac{1}{2} \qquad \cos 30° = \frac{A}{H} = \frac{\sqrt{3}}{2}$$

  $$\tan 30° = \frac{O}{A} = \frac{1}{\sqrt{3}} = \frac{\sqrt{3}}{3}$$

  iii) isosceles triangle

  $$\sin 45° = \frac{O}{H} = \frac{1}{\sqrt{2}} = \frac{\sqrt{2}}{2}$$

  $$\cos 45° = \frac{A}{H} = \frac{1}{\sqrt{2}} = \frac{\sqrt{2}}{2}$$

  $$\tan 45° = \frac{O}{A} = \frac{1}{1} = 1$$

- The unit circle is a circle with radius 1 unit. The following are true for any point P(x, y) on the unit circle and acute angle θ between OP and the x axis:

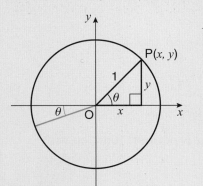

$$\sin \theta = \frac{y}{1} = y \qquad \sin 0° = 0$$

$$\cos \theta = \frac{x}{1} = x \qquad \cos 0° = 1$$

$$\tan \theta = \frac{y}{x}$$

$y^2 + x^2 = 1$ using Pythagoras' theorem

- Two important identities are $\sin^2 \theta + \cos^2 \theta = 1$ and $\tan \theta = \dfrac{\sin \theta}{\cos \theta}$.

- The angles in the anticlockwise direction from the x axis are positive and in the clockwise direction are negative.

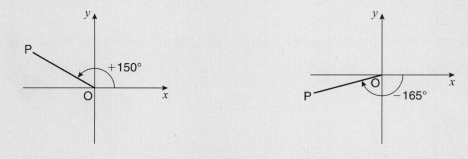

- To find sin, cos or tan of any angle you can use the unit circle method. First draw the angle and use this diagram to decide whether sin, cos or tan of this angle is positive or negative.

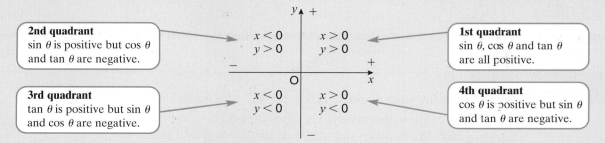

2nd quadrant
sin θ is positive but cos θ and tan θ are negative.

$x < 0$ $\quad$ $x > 0$
$y > 0$ $\quad$ $y > 0$

1st quadrant
sin θ, cos θ and tan θ are all positive.

3rd quadrant
tan θ is positive but sin θ and cos θ are negative.

$x < 0$ $\quad$ $x > 0$
$y < 0$ $\quad$ $y < 0$

4th quadrant
cos θ is positive but sin θ and tan θ are negative.

Then mark the acute angle which the line makes with the x axis.

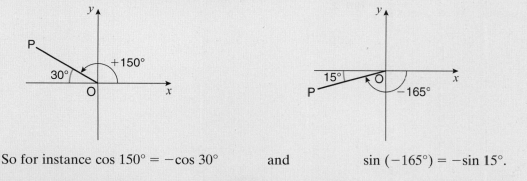

So for instance $\cos 150° = -\cos 30°$ $\qquad$ and $\qquad$ $\sin(-165°) = -\sin 15°$.

- Another way to find sin, cos or tan of any angle is to use their graphs. This tells you whether the angle is positive or negative. The symmetry of the graph gives you the equivalent acute angle (the angle between 0° and 90°).

- Graph of $y = \sin x$. The curve repeats itself every 360°. So $\sin x$ is periodic function with period 360°.

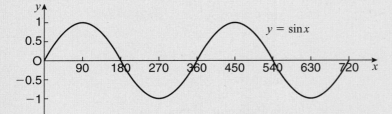

- Graph of $y = \cos x$. The curve repeats itself every 360°. So $\cos x$ is periodic function with period 360°.

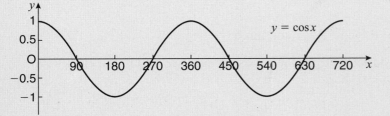

- For both $\sin x$ and $\cos x$ the maximum possible value is 1 and the minimum possible value is −1.

- Graph of $y = \tan x$. The curve repeats itself every 180°. So $\tan x$ is periodic function with period 180°.

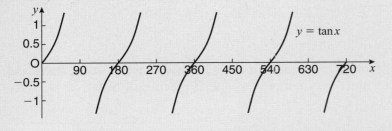

EXAMPLE 1

In the triangle ABC, AB = 13, AC = 5 and BC = 12.

i) Show that triangle is right-angled.

ii) Write down the values of $\sin B$, $\cos B$ and $\tan B$.

iii) Use your answer to part **ii)** to show that $\sin^2 B + \cos^2 B = 1$ and $\dfrac{\sin B}{\cos B} = \tan B$.

SOLUTION

i) If the triangle ABC is right-angled, the sides satisfy Pythagoras' theorem.

AB is the biggest side (the hypotenuse)

so $AB^2 = AC^2 + BC^2$

$13^2 = 5^2 + 12^2$

$169 = 25 + 144$

This is correct and so triangle ABC is right-angled.

ii)

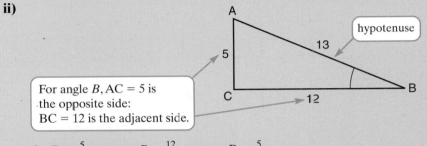

For angle B, $AC = 5$ is the opposite side:
$BC = 12$ is the adjacent side.

$\sin B = \frac{5}{13}$ $\cos B = \frac{12}{13}$ $\tan B = \frac{5}{12}$

iii) To show that $\sin^2 B + \cos^2 B = 1$

Substitute for $\sin B$ and $\cos B$ using the ratios you found in part ii)

$$\left(\frac{5}{13}\right)^2 + \left(\frac{12}{13}\right)^2 = 1$$

$\frac{25}{169} + \frac{144}{169} = 1$ is correct

$\frac{\sin B}{\cos B} = \frac{\frac{5}{13}}{\frac{12}{13}} = \frac{5}{12}$ and $\tan B = \frac{5}{12}$ so

$\frac{\sin B}{\cos B} = \tan B$ which is correct too.

EXAMPLE 2

Without using a calculator work out $\sin^2 30° - \sin^2 60° \tan^2 30°$.

$\sin^2 30°$ means $(\sin 30°)^2$.

SOLUTION

Using the trigonometrical ratios for special triangles:

$$\sin 30° = \frac{1}{2} \qquad \sin 60° = \frac{\sqrt{3}}{2} \qquad \tan 30° = \frac{1}{\sqrt{3}}$$

So $\sin^2 30° - \sin^2 60° \tan^2 30° = \left(\frac{1}{2}\right)^2 - \left(\frac{\sqrt{3}}{2}\right)^2 \times \left(\frac{1}{\sqrt{3}}\right)^2 = \frac{1}{4} - \frac{3}{4} \times \frac{1}{3} = 0$

EXAMPLE 3

Find the values of **i)** sin 300° **ii)** cos 120° **iii)** tan 395°.

SOLUTION

i) sin 300°

First draw the angle of 300°. The angle is positive so you need to draw this angle in an anticlockwise direction.

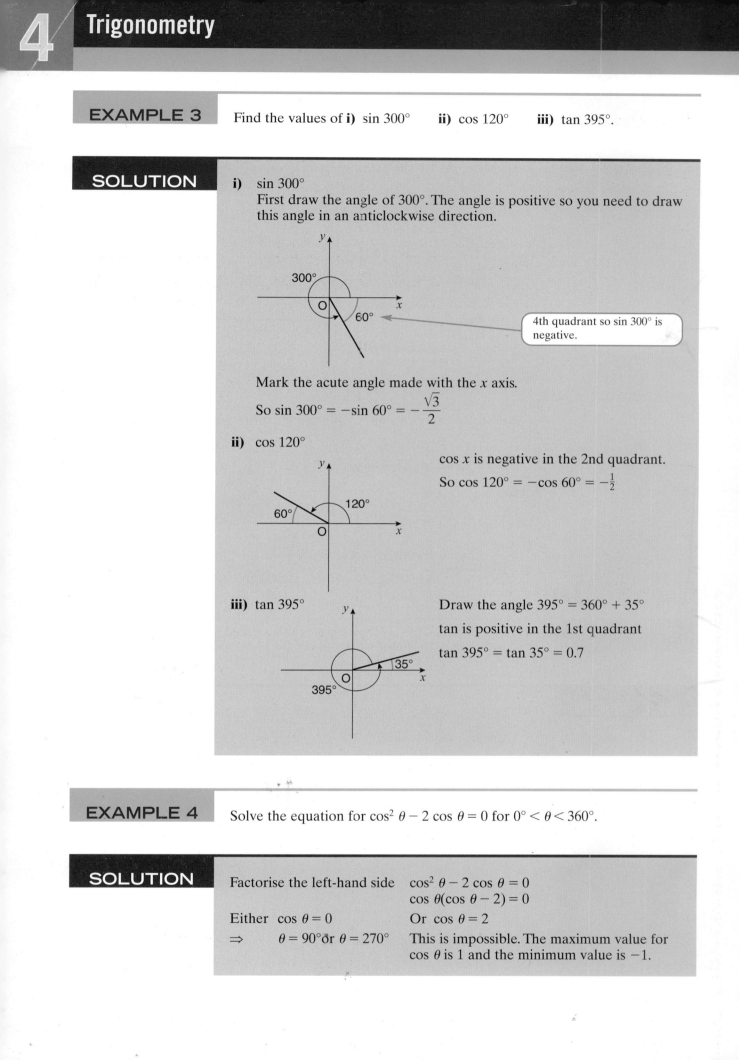

4th quadrant so sin 300° is negative.

Mark the acute angle made with the x axis.

So $\sin 300° = -\sin 60° = -\dfrac{\sqrt{3}}{2}$

ii) cos 120°

$\cos x$ is negative in the 2nd quadrant.

So $\cos 120° = -\cos 60° = -\frac{1}{2}$

iii) tan 395°

Draw the angle $395° = 360° + 35°$

tan is positive in the 1st quadrant

$\tan 395° = \tan 35° = 0.7$

EXAMPLE 4

Solve the equation for $\cos^2 \theta - 2\cos \theta = 0$ for $0° < \theta < 360°$.

SOLUTION

Factorise the left-hand side $\cos^2 \theta - 2\cos \theta = 0$

$\cos \theta(\cos \theta - 2) = 0$

Either $\cos \theta = 0$ Or $\cos \theta = 2$

$\Rightarrow$ $\theta = 90°$ or $\theta = 270°$ This is impossible. The maximum value for $\cos \theta$ is 1 and the minimum value is -1.

EXAMPLE 5 Solve $\sin(x - 65°) = \frac{1}{2}$ for $0° \leqslant x < 360°$.

SOLUTION Let $\theta = x - 65°$
From the graph of $y = \sin \theta$

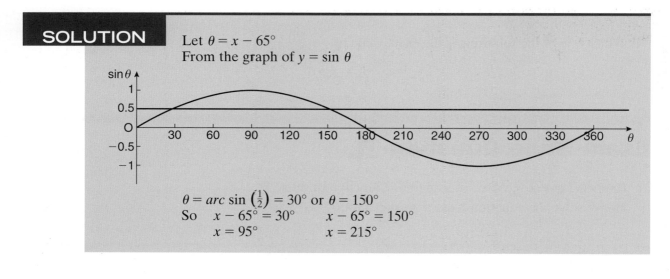

$\theta = \arcsin\left(\frac{1}{2}\right) = 30°$ or $\theta = 150°$
So $x - 65° = 30°$ $x - 65° = 150°$
           $x = 95°$ $x = 215°$

LINKS

You will use trigonometry in all branches of Mathematics, for example:
Pure Mathematics   C4.
Mechanics   Projectiles, M1.

Test Yourself ▷L

1 Four of these diagrams are correct. Which one of the diagrams is **incorrect**?

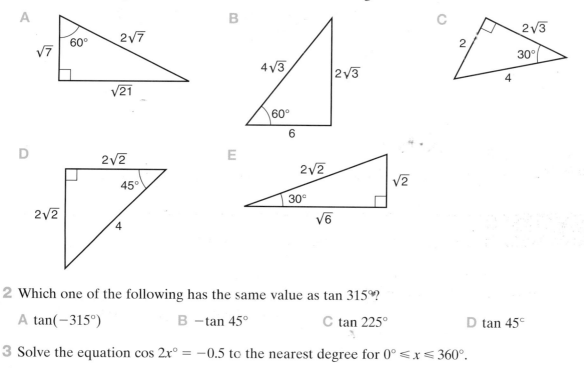

2 Which one of the following has the same value as tan 315°?

  A tan(−315°)   B −tan 45°   C tan 225°   D tan 45°

3 Solve the equation $\cos 2x° = -0.5$ to the nearest degree for $0° \leqslant x \leqslant 360°$.

  A 60°   B 60°, 120°, 240° and 300°   C 120° and 240°

  D 120°   E 60°, 120° and 240°

4 Solve the equation $\sin^2 \theta = \sin \theta$ to the nearest degree for $0° \leqslant \theta \leqslant 360°$.

A 0° and 90°   B 0°, 90°, 180° and 360°

C 0°, 180° and 360°   D 90°

5 Which one of the following is the exact value of $\dfrac{1 - \sin 240°}{1 + \sin 240°}$?

A $7 - 4\sqrt{3}$ B 1   C $7 + 4\sqrt{3}$ D 3   E 7

Exam-Style Question ▶L

a) Express $2\cos^2 x - 3\sin x$ as a quadratic function of $\sin x$.

b) Hence solve the equation $2\cos^2 x = 3\sin x$ for $0° \leqslant x \leqslant 360°$.

The sine and cosine rules

A | ABOUT THIS TOPIC

You will often need to find an angle or a length of side of a triangle that is not right-angled. The sine and cosine rules allow you to do this.

R | REMEMBER

- Bearings from GCSE.
- Trigonometrical ratios from GCSE.
- Surds from GCSE and C1.

K | KEY FACTS

- Usually the vertices of any triangle are labelled with capital letters, and the opposite sides with corresponding small letters.

- Look at the triangle ABC. Its area is given by

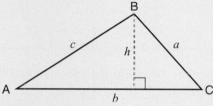

Area $= \frac{1}{2}bh$ where h is the height.

The height h splits the triangle in two right-angled triangles.
Using trigonometry:

$\sin C = \dfrac{h}{a}$ or $h = a \sin C$

substituting $h = a \sin C$
into the formula above for the area of the triangle
ABC gives

Area $= \frac{1}{2}ab \sin C$

This is a very useful formula. Equivalent formulae involving $\sin B$ and $\sin A$ are:

Area $= \frac{1}{2}ca \sin B$ and   Area $= \frac{1}{2}bc \sin A$

- Putting the three formulae for area equal to each other
$\frac{1}{2}bc \sin A = \frac{1}{2}ca \sin B = \frac{1}{2}ab \sin C$ leads to the sine rule for triangle ABC.

$$\frac{\sin A}{a} = \frac{\sin B}{b} = \frac{\sin C}{c} \qquad \text{or} \qquad \frac{a}{\sin A} = \frac{b}{\sin B} = \frac{c}{\sin C}$$

- The cosine rule for the triangle ABC is

$\cos A = \dfrac{b^2 + c^2 - a^2}{2bc}$ $a^2 = b^2 + c^2 - 2bc \cos A.$

Equivalent formulae involving $\cos B$ and $\cos C$ are:

$\cos B = \dfrac{a^2 + c^2 - b^2}{2ac}$ $b^2 = a^2 + c^2 - 2ac \cos B$

$\cos C = \dfrac{a^2 + b^2 - c^2}{2ab}$ $c^2 = a^2 + b^2 - 2ab \cos C.$

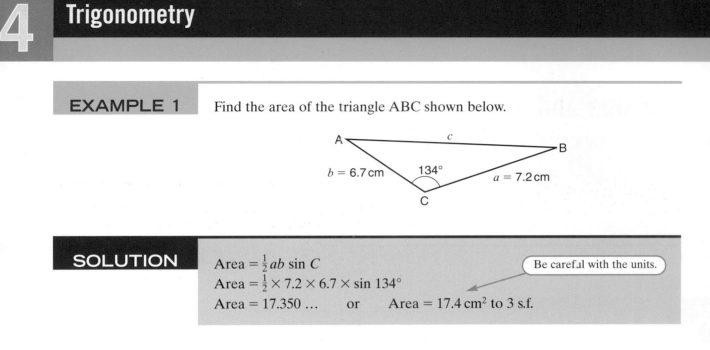

EXAMPLE 1

Find the area of the triangle ABC shown below.

SOLUTION

Area = $\frac{1}{2}ab \sin C$

Area = $\frac{1}{2} \times 7.2 \times 6.7 \times \sin 134°$

Area = 17.350 ... or Area = 17.4 cm² to 3 s.f.

> Be careful with the units.

Using the sine rule

Sometimes you need to find lengths and angles in triangles that are not right-angled. You can often do this using the sine rule, as in the next two examples.

EXAMPLE 2

Using the sine rule, find the side c in this triangle. Give your answer to the nearest 0.1 cm.

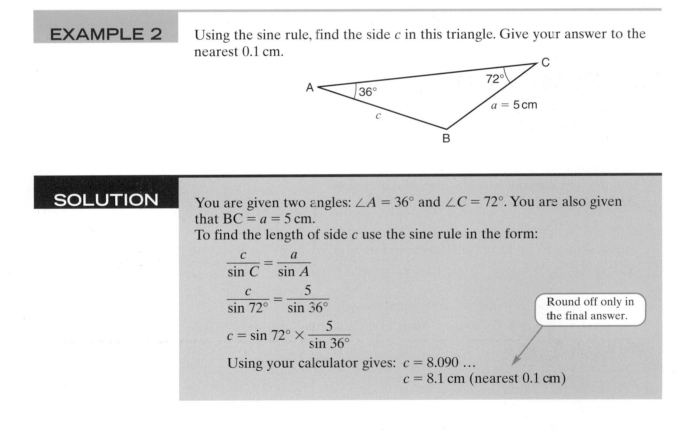

SOLUTION

You are given two angles: $\angle A = 36°$ and $\angle C = 72°$. You are also given that BC = a = 5 cm.
To find the length of side c use the sine rule in the form:

$$\frac{c}{\sin C} = \frac{a}{\sin A}$$

$$\frac{c}{\sin 72°} = \frac{5}{\sin 36°}$$

$$c = \sin 72° \times \frac{5}{\sin 36°}$$

Using your calculator gives: $c = 8.090 ...$

$c = 8.1$ cm (nearest 0.1 cm)

> Round off only in the final answer.

⚠ When the angles are given in degrees be sure that your calculator is set in degrees mode.

⚠ When you use the sine rule to find an angle there will often be two possible answers, as in the next example.

EXAMPLE 3

In triangle XZY, XZ = 3.6 cm, YZ = 4.5 cm and $\angle Y = 47°$.

i)   Draw the triangle.
ii) Find the possible size of angle X.

SOLUTION

i)   When you draw the triangle you find there are two possible angles and two possible positions for point X. These are marked X_1 and X_2.

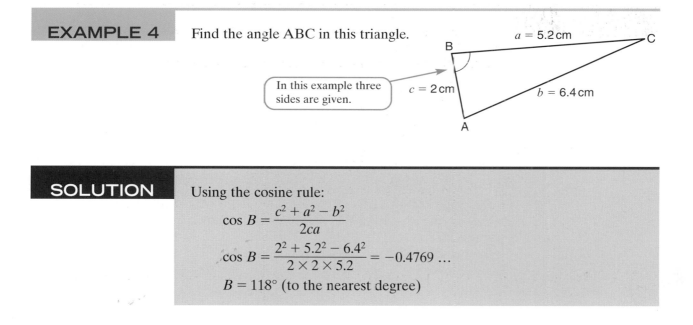

> You can see from the diagram that X lies on the circle with centre Z and radius of 3.6 cm.

ii) $\dfrac{\sin X}{4.5} = \dfrac{\sin 47°}{3.6}$

> There are two possible values of X between 0° and 180°.

$\sin X = 4.5 \times \dfrac{\sin 47°}{3.6}$

$\sin X = 0.914\,19\ldots$

$X = 66.091\ldots° \text{ or } 180° - 66.091\ldots°$

So $\angle X_1 = 66.1°$ or $\angle X_2 = 180° - 66.1° = 113.9°$ (both to the nearest 0.1°)

Using the cosine rule

Sometimes you do not have the right information to use the sine rule but can use the cosine rule to find an angle or a side of a triangle that is not right-angled.

EXAMPLE 4

Find the angle ABC in this triangle.

> In this example three sides are given.

$a = 5.2$ cm

$c = 2$ cm

$b = 6.4$ cm

SOLUTION

Using the cosine rule:

$\cos B = \dfrac{c^2 + a^2 - b^2}{2ca}$

$\cos B = \dfrac{2^2 + 5.2^2 - 6.4^2}{2 \times 2 \times 5.2} = -0.4769\ldots$

$B = 118°$ (to the nearest degree)

EXAMPLE 5

Find the length of the side p in this triangle.

SOLUTION

In this case use the cosine rule in the form: $p^2 = q^2 + r^2 - 2qr \cos P$

$p^2 = 5^2 + 3.4^2 - 2 \times 5 \times 3.4 \times \cos 38°$

$p^2 = 9.767\,634\,377\ldots$

$p = 3.13$ (to 3 s.f.)

EXAMPLE 6

Ship A is 3 km from a lighthouse L on a bearing 137°. Ship B is 6.5 km from the lighthouse on a bearing 067°. Find the distance and bearing of ship A from ship B.

SOLUTION

You need to find the distance AB and the angle NBA.

First look at angle ALB. It is $137° - 67° = 70°$

Now use the cosine rule in the triangle ALB.

$AB^2 = 6.5^2 + 3^2 - 2 \times 6.5 \times 3 \cos 70°$
$AB = 6.1572 \ldots$

> Round off only in the final answer.

> $\angle ALB = 70°$

The bearing of ship A from ship B is angle NBA (shown in orange).

First find $\angle ABL$ using sine rule $\dfrac{\sin B}{3} = \dfrac{\sin 70°}{6.1572\ldots}$

> Round off only in the final answer.

$\sin B = 3 \times \dfrac{\sin 70°}{6.1572\ldots} = 0.4578\ldots$

$\angle B = 27.248\ldots$

> Notice that
> $\angle NBA = 360° - (\angle ABL + \angle LBN)$.
> So start by finding $\angle ABL$ and $\angle LBN$.

The angle LBN is $180° - 67° = 113°$
The bearing of A from B is the reflex angle shown in orange.
This is $360° - (113° + 27.25°) = 219.75°$.
The bearing is 220° to the nearest degree.

LINKS

Mechanics   Force and Velocity Triangles.

Test Yourself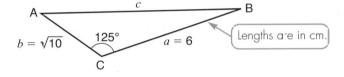

1 In the triangle ABC, $\angle CAB = 37°$, $\angle ABC = 56°$ and $CB = 4$ cm. Find the length of AC.

   A 3.24 cm   B 8.02 cm   C 5.51 cm   D 0.18 cm   E 2.90 cm

2 In the triangle XYZ, $XY = 3.8$ cm, $YZ = 4.5$ cm and $\angle YZX = 40°$. Three of the following statements are false and one is true. Which one is true?

   A A possible value for the area of the triangle is exactly 8.55 cm².

   B The only possible value of $\angle XYZ$ is 90° to the nearest degree.

   C You can find the remaining side and angles of the triangle using only the cosine rule.

   D The possible values of $\angle YXZ$ are 50° and 130° (to the nearest degree).

3 In the triangle MNP, $MN = 5.4$ cm, $NP = 6$ cm and $MP = 7$ cm. Find angle MNP correct to 3 s.f.

   A 48.3°   B 75.6°   C 56.1°   D 1.32°

4 For this triangle three of the statements are true and one is false. Which one is false?

   A The area of the triangle is 7.77 cm² (to 3 s.f.).

   B AB is 8.23 cm (to 3 s.f.).

   C Using only the sine rule you can find the value of c.

   D $\angle B = 18.34°$ (to 2 d.p.).

5 At 12 noon a ship is at a point M which is on a bearing 148° from a lighthouse, L. The ship travels due east at 20 km h⁻¹ and at 1230 hours it is at point N, on a bearing of 127° from the lighthouse. Three of the following statements are false and one is true. Which one is true?

   A At 1230 hours the ship is 17 km from the lighthouse.

   B The area LMN is 100 km², to the nearest whole number.

   C At noon the ship is 16.8 km from L to the nearest kilometre.

   D If the ship continues on the same speed and the same course, it will be on a bearing of 106° from the lighthouse at 1300 hours.

Exam-Style Question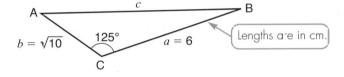

In a quadrilateral ABCD, $AD = 7$ cm, $DC = 5$ cm, $\angle ADC = 47°$, $\angle ABC = 127°$ and $\angle BAC = 35°$.

i)   Find the length of AC.

ii)   Find the angle CAD.

iii)   Find the length of AB.

iv)   Find the area of the quadrilateral.

Radians

A ABOUT THIS TOPIC

Have you ever wondered why angles are measured in degrees, and why there are 360° in one revolution? Why are there are different measures for an angle on your calculator? What are radians?

When you use trigonometrical functions in calculus – and you will do this a lot – then angles have to be in radians. So it is important to get used to working in them.

R REMEMBER

- Trigonometrical ratios from GCSE and M1.
- Surds from GCSE and C1.
- Area of a triangle from GCSE and C2.
- Arcs and sectors from GCSE.

K KEY FACTS

- Arcs:

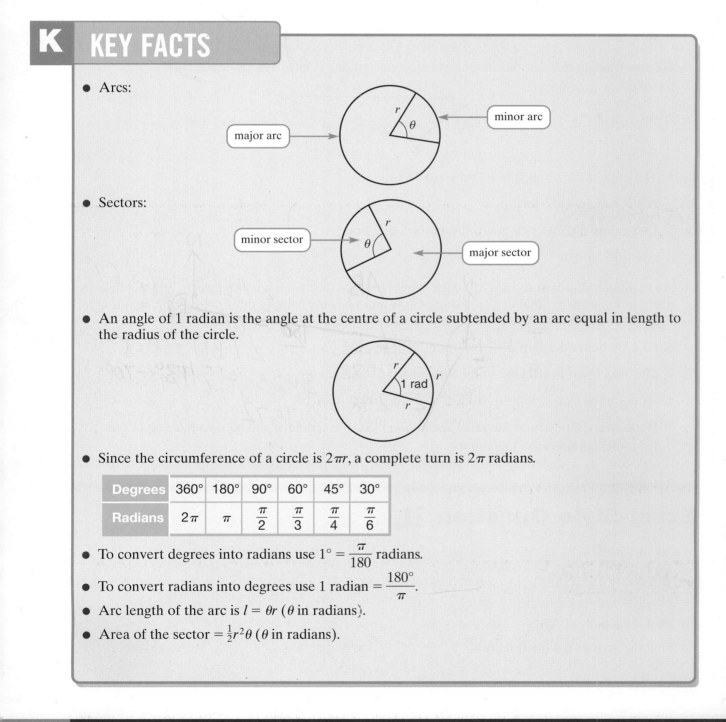

- Sectors:

- An angle of 1 radian is the angle at the centre of a circle subtended by an arc equal in length to the radius of the circle.

- Since the circumference of a circle is $2\pi r$, a complete turn is 2π radians.

Degrees	360°	180°	90°	60°	45°	30°
Radians	2π	π	$\frac{\pi}{2}$	$\frac{\pi}{3}$	$\frac{\pi}{4}$	$\frac{\pi}{6}$

- To convert degrees into radians use $1° = \dfrac{\pi}{180}$ radians.

- To convert radians into degrees use $1 \text{ radian} = \dfrac{180°}{\pi}$.

- Arc length of the arc is $l = \theta r$ (θ in radians).

- Area of the sector $= \frac{1}{2} r^2 \theta$ (θ in radians).

Trigonometry

EXAMPLE 1

Express the following angles in radians, leaving your answers in terms of π where appropriate:

i) $23°$ ii) $120°$ iii) $150°$ iv) $207°$

SOLUTION

To convert degrees into radians use $1° = \dfrac{\pi}{180}$ radians and so multiply by $\dfrac{\pi}{180}$.

> You cannot cancel down 23 and 180. Write this as a decimal.

i) $23° \times \dfrac{\pi}{180} = 0.401\,425\,728$ or $23° = 0.401$ radians (to 3 s.f.)

ii) $120° \times \dfrac{\pi}{180} = 2 \times \dfrac{\pi}{3}$ or $120° = \dfrac{2\pi}{3}$ radians

iii) $150° \times \dfrac{\pi}{180} = 5 \times \dfrac{\pi}{6}$ or $150° = \dfrac{5\pi}{6}$ radians

iv) $207° \times \dfrac{\pi}{180} = 3.612\,831\,552$ or $207° = 3.6\underline{}$ radians (to 3 s.f.)

EXAMPLE 2

Express the following angles in degrees, using suitable approximation where necessary.

i) $\dfrac{\pi}{9}$ ii) 3 rad   iii) 5π.

SOLUTION

To convert radians into degrees, use 1 radian $= \dfrac{180}{\pi}$ degrees so multiply by $\dfrac{180°}{\pi}$.

So

i) $\dfrac{\pi}{9} \times \dfrac{180°}{\pi} = 20°$ or $\dfrac{\pi}{9} = 20°$

ii) $3 \times \dfrac{180°}{\pi} = 171.887\,\ldots$ or 3 rad $= 171.9°$ to the nearest 0.1 degree

iii) $5\pi \times \dfrac{180°}{\pi} = 900°$ or $5\pi = 900°$

EXAMPLE 3

Without using your calculator evaluate the following:

i) $\sin \dfrac{\pi}{4}$ ii) $\tan \dfrac{\pi}{4}$ iii) $\cos \dfrac{\pi}{3}$ iv) $\sin \dfrac{2\pi}{3}$

SOLUTION

Notice that $\dfrac{\pi}{4} = 45°$ $\dfrac{\pi}{3} = 60°$ $\dfrac{2\pi}{3} = 120°$

So

i) $\sin \dfrac{\pi}{4} = \dfrac{1}{\sqrt{2}}$ ii) $\tan \dfrac{\pi}{4} = 1$ iii) $\cos \dfrac{\pi}{3} = 0.5$ iv) $\sin \dfrac{2\pi}{3} = \dfrac{\sqrt{3}}{2}$

You need to remember the trigonometrical ratios for these angles.

	$0° = 0$	$30° = \dfrac{\pi}{6}$	$45° = \dfrac{\pi}{4}$	$60° = \dfrac{\pi}{3}$	$90° = \dfrac{\pi}{2}$
$\sin\theta$	0	$\dfrac{1}{2}$	$\dfrac{\sqrt{2}}{2}$	$\dfrac{\sqrt{3}}{2}$	1
$\cos\theta$	1	$\dfrac{\sqrt{3}}{2}$	$\dfrac{\sqrt{2}}{2}$	$\dfrac{1}{2}$	0
$\tan\theta$	0	$\dfrac{1}{\sqrt{3}}$	1	$\sqrt{3}$	∞

EXAMPLE 4

Solve the following equations for $-\pi < \theta < \pi$. ← Notice the use of π here. It tells you to work in radians.

i) $\cos\theta = 0.74$

ii) $\tan^2\theta = 3$

SOLUTION

i) $\cos\theta = 0.74$

$\theta = 0.637\ldots$ or $\theta = -0.637\ldots$ ← Be sure that your calculator is in radians mode.

$\theta = 0.64$ (to 2 d.p.) or $\theta = -0.64$ (to 2 d.p.)

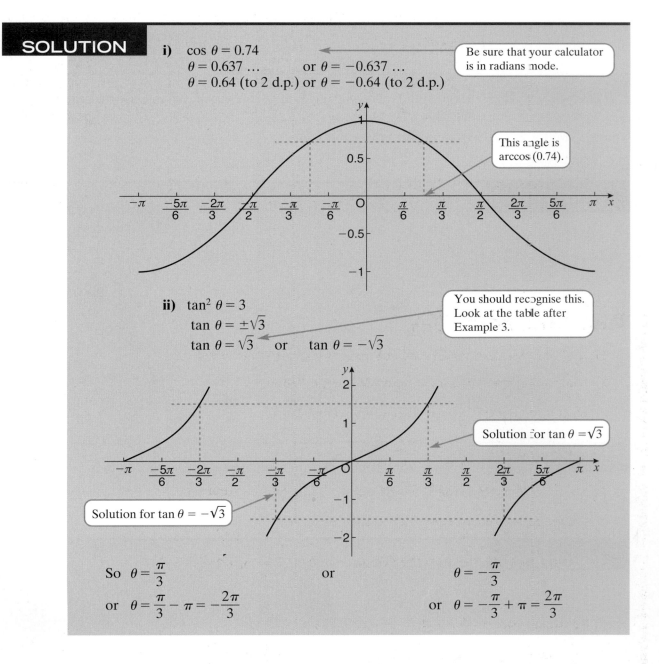

This angle is arccos (0.74).

ii) $\tan^2\theta = 3$

$\tan\theta = \pm\sqrt{3}$

$\tan\theta = \sqrt{3}$ or $\tan\theta = -\sqrt{3}$

You should recognise this. Look at the table after Example 3.

Solution for $\tan\theta = \sqrt{3}$

Solution for $\tan\theta = -\sqrt{3}$

So $\theta = \dfrac{\pi}{3}$ or $\theta = -\dfrac{\pi}{3}$

or $\theta = \dfrac{\pi}{3} - \pi = -\dfrac{2\pi}{3}$ or $\theta = -\dfrac{\pi}{3} + \pi = \dfrac{2\pi}{3}$

EXAMPLE 5

For the given sector calculate:

i)   the arc length
ii) the perimeter
iii) the area.

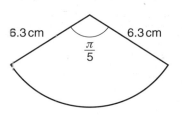

6.3 cm $\dfrac{\pi}{5}$ 6.3 cm

SOLUTION

i)   The arc length $= r\theta$

$$= 6.3 \times \frac{\pi}{5}$$
$$= 3.958 \ldots$$
$$= 3.96 \text{ cm (to 3 s.f.)}$$

> Keep the result without rounding it off. You will need it to calculate the perimeter.

ii) The perimeter $= 3.958 \ldots + 6.3 + 6.3$
$$= 16.558 \ldots$$
$$= 16.6 \text{ cm (to 3 s.f.)}$$

iii) Area $= \frac{1}{2}r^2\theta$
$$= \frac{1}{2} \times (6.3)^2 \times \frac{\pi}{5}$$
$$= 12.468 \ldots$$
$$= 12.5 \text{ cm}^2 \text{ (to 3 s.f.)}$$

LINKS

Pure Mathematics: Calculus with Trigonometrical Functions (C3, C4).
Solving Trigonometrical Equations (C4).

Test Yourself

1 Four of the statements below are false and one is true. Which one is true?

A   When you convert $540°$ into radians the answer is 6π.

B   When you convert $\dfrac{7\pi}{15}$ into degrees the answer is $84°$.

C $\left(\tan \dfrac{\pi}{4} - \cos \dfrac{\pi}{2}\right) = \left(\cos \dfrac{\pi}{2} - \tan \dfrac{\pi}{4}\right)$

D $\cos \dfrac{5\pi}{6}$ is the same as $\cos 150°$ and the result is a positive number.

E $\sin(\pi + \theta) = \sin \theta$ is true for all values of θ.

2 How many roots are there for the equation $\sin \theta = \dfrac{1}{\sqrt{2}}$ for $-2\pi \leqslant \theta \leqslant 2\pi$?

A 2   B 3   C 1   D 4

3 Solve the equation $2 \sin^2 x = 1$, for $-\pi < x < \pi$.

A $-\dfrac{\pi}{4}$ and $\dfrac{\pi}{4}$ B $\dfrac{\pi}{4}$ and $\dfrac{3\pi}{4}$ C $\pm\dfrac{\pi}{4}$ and $\pm\dfrac{3\pi}{4}$ D 0

4 Here are four statements about the sector of a circle with radius r cm. The angle subtended at the centre of the circle is θ radians, the arc length of the sector is l cm and its area is A cm². Three of the statements are false and one is true. Which one is true?

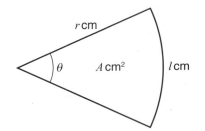

A When $r = 6$ and $\theta = \dfrac{\pi}{3}$, then $l = 2\pi$ and $A = 12\pi$.

B When $r = 8$ and $l = \dfrac{\pi}{3}$, then $\theta = \dfrac{1}{24}\pi$ and $A = 240$.

C When $\theta = 0.6$ and $l = 2.4$, then $r = 4$ and $A = 4.8$.

D When $r = 2\sqrt{2}$ and $l = 2$, then $A = 2\sqrt{2}$ and $\theta = \sqrt{2}$.

Exam-Style Question ▷L

The figure on the right shows a circle with centre O and radius 12.6 cm. ST and RT are tangents to the circle and the angle SOR is 1.82 radians.

i) Show that ST = 16.2 cm to 3 significant figures.

ii) Find the area and perimeter of the shaded shape, SRT.

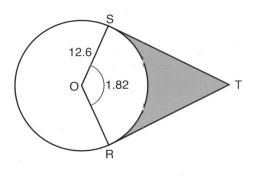

Transformations of curves

A ABOUT THIS TOPIC

Being able to start with a simple curve and use it to derive the shape of one with more complicated equation is a very important mathematical skill. It is often used when the form of the curve is trigonometrical, particularly the sine wave.

R REMEMBER

- Transformations of functions from C1 and GCSE.
- Sketching $y = \sin x$, $y = \cos x$ and $y = \tan x$ from C1 and GCSE.

K KEY FACTS

- Transformations of $y = f(x)$ are:

Reflections

in x axis
$y = -f(x)$

in y axis
$y = f(-x)$

Translations (for positive a)

parallel to x axis

$y = f(x - a)$ $\begin{pmatrix} a \\ 0 \end{pmatrix}$

(a units to the right)

$y = f(x + a)$ $\begin{pmatrix} -a \\ 0 \end{pmatrix}$

(a units to the left)

parallel to y axis

$y = f(x) + a$ $\begin{pmatrix} 0 \\ a \end{pmatrix}$

(a units up)

$y = f(x) - a$ $\begin{pmatrix} 0 \\ -a \end{pmatrix}$

(a units down)

Stretches

parallel to x axis

$y = f(ax)$ scale factor $\dfrac{1}{a}$

parallel to y axis

$y = af(x)$ scale factor a

EXAMPLE 1

Starting with the curve $y = \sin \theta$, describe and show how transformations can be used to sketch these curves:

i) $y = \sin \theta + 2$
ii) $y = 3 \sin \theta$
iii) $y = -\sin \theta$
iv) $y = \sin(30° + \theta)$
v) $y = \sin \dfrac{\theta}{2}$.

SOLUTION

i) The curve $y = \sin \theta + 2$ is obtained from the curve $y = \sin \theta$ by a translation $\begin{pmatrix} 0 \\ 2 \end{pmatrix}$. The curve $y = \sin \theta + 2$ oscillates between a minimum of $y = 1$ and a maximum of $y = 3$.

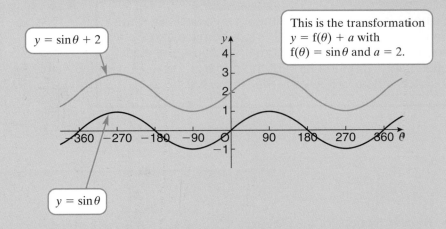

$y = \sin \theta + 2$

This is the transformation $y = f(\theta) + a$ with $f(\theta) = \sin \theta$ and $a = 2$.

$y = \sin \theta$

ii) The curve $y = 3 \sin \theta$ is obtained from the curve $y = \sin \theta$ by a stretch with the scale factor 3, parallel to the y axis. The curve $y = 3 \sin \theta$ oscillates between a minimum of $y = -3$ and a maximum of $y = 3$.

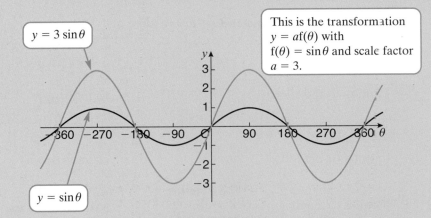

$y = 3 \sin \theta$

This is the transformation $y = af(\theta)$ with $f(\theta) = \sin \theta$ and scale factor $a = 3$.

$y = \sin \theta$

iii) The curve $y = -\sin \theta$ is obtained from the curve $y = \sin \theta$ by reflection on the x axis. The curve $y = -\sin \theta$ oscillates between a minimum of $y = -1$ and a maximum of $y = 1$.

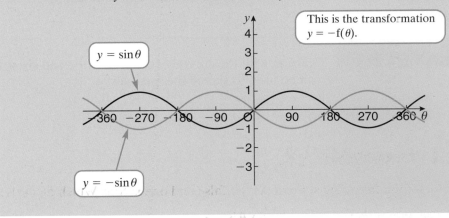

$y = \sin \theta$

This is the transformation $y = -f(\theta)$.

$y = -\sin \theta$

iv) The curve $y = \sin(30° + \theta)$ is obtained from the curve $y = \sin \theta$ by translation $\begin{pmatrix} -30° \\ 0 \end{pmatrix}$ or 30° to the left along the x axis. The curve $y = \sin(\theta + 30°)$ oscillates between a minimum of $y = -1$ and a maximum of $y = 1$.

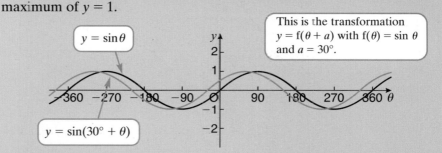

$y = \sin \theta$

This is the transformation $y = f(\theta + a)$ with $f(\theta) = \sin \theta$ and $a = 30°$.

$y = \sin(30° + \theta)$

v) The curve $y = \sin \dfrac{\theta}{2}$ is obtained from the curve $y = \sin \theta$ by a stretch of the scale factor 2. The curve $y = \sin \dfrac{\theta}{2}$ oscillates between a minimum of $y = -1$ and a maximum of $y = 1$.

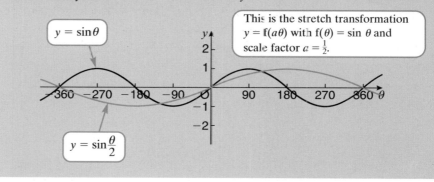

$y = \sin \theta$

This is the stretch transformation $y = f(a\theta)$ with $f(\theta) = \sin \theta$ and scale factor $a = \frac{1}{2}$.

$y = \sin \dfrac{\theta}{2}$

LINKS

Pure Mathematics	Solving Trigonometrical Equations (C4).
Mechanics	Simple Harmonic Motion (M3).
Differential Equations	Oscillations (DE).

Test Yourself ▷L

1 Three of the following statements are false and one is true. Which one is true?

A The minimum value of $y = \frac{1}{3} \sin \theta$ is -3.

B The curve of $y = \sin 3\theta$ oscillates between -3 and 3.

C $y = \tan\left(\theta - \dfrac{\pi}{3}\right)$ is a periodic function, with the period of 2π.

D The minimum value of $y = \sin 2\theta$ is -1.

2 Which of the following is the curve of $y = \tan x + 2$ for $0 \le x \le \pi$?

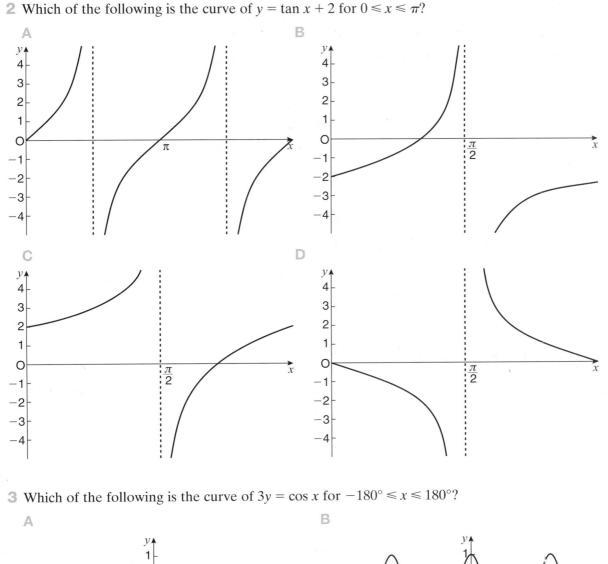

A

B

C

D

3 Which of the following is the curve of $3y = \cos x$ for $-180° \le x \le 180°$?

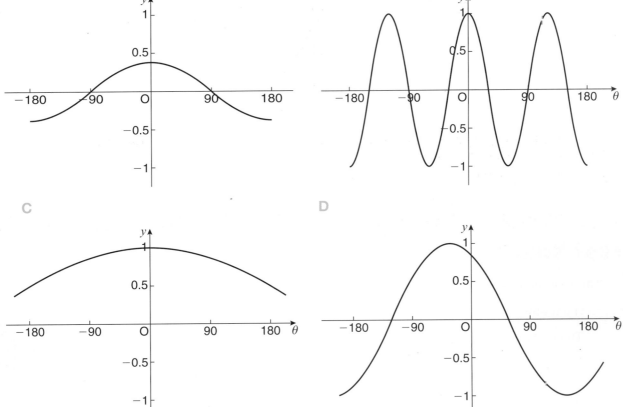

A

B

C

D

4 Four of the statements below are false and one is true. Which one is true?

A The graph of $y = \sin(x - 90°)$ is the same as the graph of $y = \cos x$.

B The graph below is the same as the graph of $y = \sin(x + 60°)$.

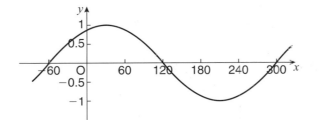

C The graph of $y = -\cos x$ is the same as the graph of $y = \cos x$.

D The graph of $y = \sin(x + 180°)$ is the same as the graph of $y = \sin x$.

E The graph of $y = \sin(x - 45°)$ is the same as the graph of $y = \cos(x + 45°)$.

Exam-Style Question ▷L

The diagram shows the graph of $y = f(x)$ which has a maximum point at $(-3, 3)$, a minimum point at $(3, -3)$, and passes through the origin.

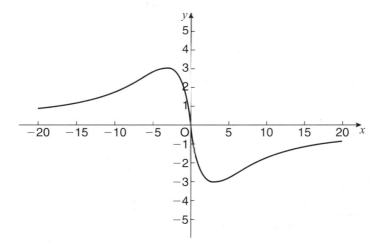

Sketch the following graphs, using a separate set of axes for each graph, and indicating the co-ordinates of the turning points.

i) $y = 2f(x)$ ii) $y = f(2x)$ iii) $y = f(x) + 2$.

Logarithms and exponentials

Logarithms and exponential functions

A ABOUT THIS TOPIC

This topic builds on your knowledge of indices from C1. After studying this you will be able to manipulate and simplify numerical and algebraic expressions which contain logarithms.

Index is another word for power. The plural of index is indices.

R REMEMBER

- Laws of indices from C1.

K KEY FACTS

- $f(x) = a^x$ is an exponential function
- $y = \log_a x \Leftrightarrow a^y = x$
- For logarithms to any base

  Multiplication: $\log xy = \log x + \log y$

  Powers: $\log x^n = n \log x$

  Logarithm of 1: $\log 1 = 0$

  Division: $\log \dfrac{x}{y} = \log x - \log y$

  Roots: $\log \sqrt[n]{x} = \dfrac{1}{n} \log x$

  Reciprocals: $\log \dfrac{1}{x} = -\log x$

- Logarithm to its own base: $\log_a a = 1$

Logarithms

Since $16 = 2^4$, $\log_2 16 = \log_2(2^4) = 4$. You can say that the logarithm to base 2 of 16 is 4, so logarithm is another name for a power. Logarithm is usually abbreviated to log so you would write $\log_2 16 = 4$.

> Notice that you write the base of the logarithm as a subscript.

EXAMPLE 1	Find the logarithm to base 3 of 243.

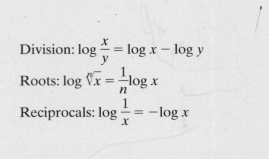

SOLUTION	$243 = 3^5$ so $\log_3 243 = \log_3(3^5) = 5$

EXAMPLE 2 Find the logarithm to base 5 of $\sqrt{5}$.

SOLUTION $\sqrt{5} = 5^{\frac{1}{2}}$ so $\log_5 \sqrt{5} = \log_5 5^{\frac{1}{2}} = \frac{1}{2}$

EXAMPLE 3 Write the values of the following

i) $\log_{10} 100\,000$ **ii)** $\log_5 125$ **iii)** $\log_9 3$ **iv)** $\log_3 \frac{1}{27}$ **v)** $\log_2 \sqrt{8}$

SOLUTION

i) $100\,000 = 10^5$
$\log_{10} 100\,000 = 5$

ii) $125 = 5^3$
$\log_5 125 = 3$

iii) $3 = 9^{\frac{1}{2}}$
$\log_9 3 = \frac{1}{2}$

iv) $27 = 3^3 \Rightarrow \frac{1}{27} = \frac{1}{3^3} = 3^{-3}$
$\log_3 \frac{1}{27} = \log_3 (3^{-3}) = -3$

v) $\sqrt{8} = (2^3)^{\frac{1}{2}} = 2^{\frac{3}{2}}$
$\log_2 \sqrt{8} = \log_2 2^{\frac{3}{2}} = \frac{3}{2}$

Laws of logarithms

Since a logarithm is a power, the laws of logarithms follow from the laws of indices.

$\log xy = \log x + \log y$ $\log \frac{x}{y} = \log x - \log y$

$\log x^n = n\log x$ $\log \sqrt[n]{x} = \frac{1}{n}\log x$

⚠️ Remember that $\log 1 = 0$ in any base.

EXAMPLE 4 Write $\log 10 + \log 4$ in the form $\log x$.

SOLUTION Using $\log x + \log y = \log xy$, $\log 10 + \log 4 = \log(10 \times 4) = \log 40$

EXAMPLE 5 Write $\frac{1}{2} \log 81 - \log 3$ in the form $\log x$ where the number x is to be determined.

SOLUTION Using $n\log x = \log x^n$, $\frac{1}{2} \log 81 - \log 3 = \log 81^{\frac{1}{2}} - \log 3 = \log 9 - \log 3$

Using $\log x - \log y = \log \frac{x}{y}$,

$\log 9 - \log 3 = \log \left(\frac{9}{3}\right) = \log 3$

EXAMPLE 6

Express $\log x^{\frac{2}{3}}$ in terms of $\log x$.

SOLUTION

Using $\log x^n = n\log x$, $\log x^{\frac{2}{3}} = \frac{2}{3}\log x$

EXAMPLE 7

Express $\log x^7 - 3 \log x$ as a single logarithm.

SOLUTION

$\log x^7 - 3 \log x = 7 \log x - 3 \log x = 4 \log x$

Solving equations using logarithms

You can use logarithms to solve equations such as $3^n = 4200$ by taking logarithms to base 10 of both sides and then working out the answer using a calculator.

A ADVICE

There are two buttons on the calculator, log and ln.
Log gives logarithms to base 10 ($\log_{10}$) and ln gives logarithms to base e, ln $= \log_e$ (these are called natural logarithms; you meet them in C3). For the calculations in this chapter you will be using $\log_{10}$ so you should use the log button.

EXAMPLE 8

Use logarithms to base 10 to solve the equation $3^n = 4200$, giving your answer to two decimal places.

SOLUTION

$$3^n = 4200$$

Take logs of both sides
$$\log_{10} 3^n = \log_{10} 4200$$
$$n\log_{10} 3 = \log_{10} 4200$$

Divide both sides by log 3
$$n = \frac{\log_{10} 4200}{\log_{10} 3}$$

Use a calculator to work out the answer
$$n = 7.59 \ (2 \ \text{d.p.})$$

Exponential functions

Look at the graphs of $y = 2^x$ and $y = \log_2 x$

The graph of $y = 2^x$
- goes through $(0, 1)$
- only exists for positive values of y.

Now notice that the graph of $y = \log_2 x$
- goes through $(1, 0)$
- only exists for positive values of x.

$y = 2^x$ is called an exponential function.
$y = \log_2 x$ is the inverse function of $y = 2^x$.
$y = \log_2 x$ is the reflection of $y = 2^x$ in the line $y = x$.
This is true for any base a, not just 2; the graph of
$y = \log_a x$ is the reflection of $y = a^x$ in the line $y = x$
$\log_a (a^x) = x$ and
$a^{\log_a x} = x$

The graph of $y = \log_a x$ looks like $y = \log_2 x$.
It goes through $(1, 0)$ and $(a, 1)$.

EXAMPLE 9

Solve the equation $2 \log_{10} x - \log_{10} 5 = \log_{10} 15$ giving your answer to two decimal places.

SOLUTION

Add $\log_{10} 5$ to both sides	$2 \log_{10} x - \log_{10} 5 = \log_{10} 15$
	$2 \log_{10} x = \log_{10} 15 + \log_{10} 5$
	$2 \log_{10} x = \log_{10} (15 \times 5)$
Laws of logarithms: addition	$2 \log_{10} x = \log_{10} 75$
Laws of logarithms: powers	$\log_{10} x^2 = \log_{10} 75$
	$x^2 = 75$
	$x = \sqrt{75} = \pm 8.66 \ (2 \text{ d.p.})$

EXAMPLE 10

How many terms are there in the geometric sequence $2, 8, 32 \ldots 2\,097\,152$?

SOLUTION

The first term $a = 2$ and the common ratio $r = 4$.

The nth term of a geometric sequence is given by $a_n = ar^{n-1}$ so
$2\,097\,152 = 2 \times 4^{n-1} \Rightarrow 1\,048\,576 = 4^{n-1}$

$\Rightarrow \log 1\,048\,576 = \log 4^{n-1} \Rightarrow \log 1\,048\,576 = (n-1) \log 4$

$\Rightarrow \dfrac{\log 1\,048\,576}{\log 4} = n - 1$

$10 = n - 1 \Rightarrow 11 = n$

So the geometric sequence has 11 terms.

LINKS

These are basic algebraic techniques which are used extensively in all the Pure and Applied Mathematics modules.

Pure Mathematics   Natural Logarithms and Exponentials (C3).
                               Differentiation (C2, C3).
                               Integration (C2, C3, C4).
                               Complex Numbers (FP2).

Test Yourself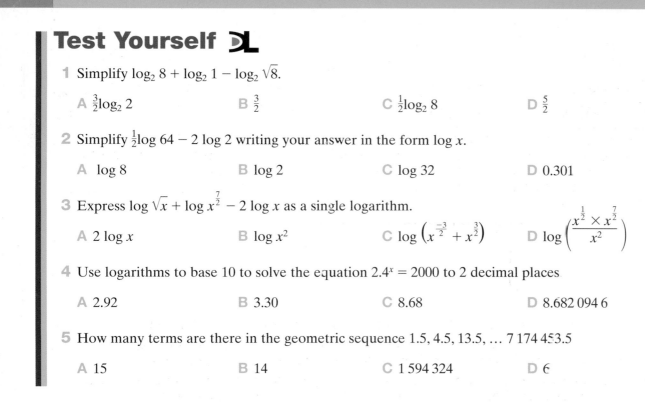

1 Simplify $\log_2 8 + \log_2 1 - \log_2 \sqrt{8}$.

    A $\frac{3}{2}\log_2 2$ B $\frac{3}{2}$ C $\frac{1}{2}\log_2 8$ D $\frac{5}{2}$

2 Simplify $\frac{1}{2}\log 64 - 2\log 2$ writing your answer in the form $\log x$.

    A $\log 8$ B $\log 2$ C $\log 32$ D 0.301

3 Express $\log \sqrt{x} + \log x^{\frac{7}{2}} - 2\log x$ as a single logarithm.

    A $2\log x$ B $\log x^2$ C $\log\left(x^{\frac{-3}{2}} + x^{\frac{3}{2}}\right)$ D $\log\left(\dfrac{x^{\frac{1}{2}} \times x^{\frac{7}{2}}}{x^2}\right)$

4 Use logarithms to base 10 to solve the equation $2.4^x = 2000$ to 2 decimal places.

    A 2.92 B 3.30 C 8.68 D $8.682\,094\,6$

5 How many terms are there in the geometric sequence $1.5, 4.5, 13.5, \ldots 7\,174\,453.5$

    A 15 B 14 C $1\,594\,324$ D 6

Exam-Style Question

a)   i)   Express $\log_a \dfrac{1}{\rho^2} + \log_a \rho^5$ as a multiple of $\log_a \rho$

    ii)   Hence solve the equations

      A $\log_{10} \dfrac{1}{\rho^2} + \log_{10} \rho^5 = 9$

      B $\log_2 \dfrac{1}{\rho^2} + \log_2 \rho^5 = 9$

b)   Solve the equation $\log z + \log(z - 2) = \log 3$

Modelling curves

This topic builds on your knowledge of logarithms and exponential functions. After studying this you will be able to use logarithms and exponentials to establish a mathematical relationship between variables for experimental data.

- Laws of indices from C1.
- Laws of logarithms from C2.

- Logarithms can be used to find the relationship between variables in two situations.
  1 For relationships of the form $y = kx^n$, $\log_{10} y = n\log_{10}x + \log_{10}k$ and so plotting $\log y$ against $\log x$ gives a straight line. The gradient of the line is n and the intercept is $\log k$.
  2 For relationships of the form $y = ka^x$, $\log_{10} y = x\log_{10}a + \log_{10}k$ and so plotting $\log y$ against x gives a straight line. The gradient of the line is $\log a$ and the intercept is $\log k$.

- In the exam, you will usually be told which type of relationship to use.

- Plot the points as accurately as possible and then draw a line of best fit.

- Logarithms can be to any base, but only those to base 10 are required in C2.

- Most calculators have a button that says 'LOG'. This means log to base 10.

Modelling

Logarithmic functions can sometimes be used to find a relationship between variables obtained from experiments.

Plotting $\log y$ against $\log x$

In an experiment, values of two variables (say x and y) are measured. You want to find a relationship between them so a useful first step is to draw a graph of y against x. If the results do not lie on a straight line it can be useful to plot $\log y$ against $\log x$ to see whether this gives a straight line.

If the relationship is of the form $y = kx^n$, the graph of $\log_{10} y$ against $\log_{10} x$ will be a straight line with n as the gradient and $\log k$ as the intercept.

$$y = kx^n$$
$$\Rightarrow \log_{10} y = \log_{10} kx^n$$
$$\Rightarrow \log_{10} y = \log_{10} x^n + \log_{10} k$$
$$\Rightarrow \log_{10} y = n\log_{10} x + \log_{10} k$$

Using the laws of logarithms.

Notice that this is the equation of a straight line, $y = mx + c$.

EXAMPLE 1

In an experiment the temperature $\theta\,°C$ of a cooling liquid is measured every 2 minutes. The table shows the results.

Time in minutes (t)	2	4	6	8	10
Temperature (θ)	95	65	56	38	31

i) Plot the graph of $\log_{10} \theta$ against $\log_{10} t$ and draw a line of best fit.
ii) Use the graph to find the relationship between θ and t.
iii) Use the equation in part ii) to predict the temperature of the liquid after 15 minutes, giving your answer to one decimal place.
iv) At what time, to the nearest minute, will the temperature of the liquid be $40\,°C$?

SOLUTION

i) Make a table to show $\log_{10} t$ and $\log_{10} \theta$ then plot the graph of $\log_{10} \theta$ against $\log_{10} t$

> The graph is a straight line, so you can use it to find a relationship between θ and t since you know that the equation of a straight line is $y = mx + c$.

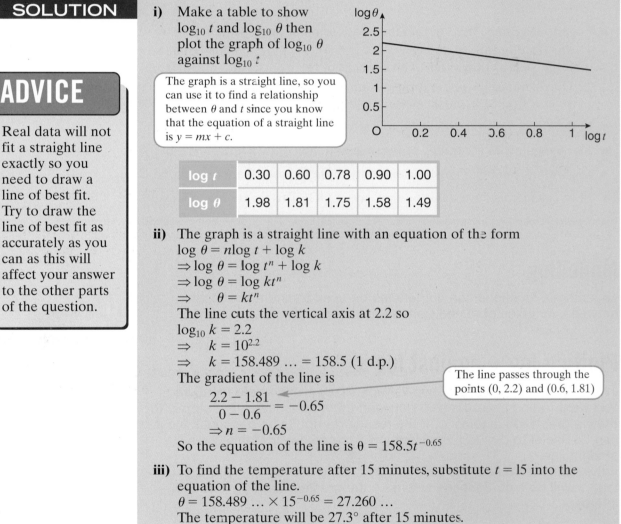

log t	0.30	0.60	0.78	0.90	1.00
log θ	1.98	1.81	1.75	1.58	1.49

ADVICE

Real data will not fit a straight line exactly so you need to draw a line of best fit. Try to draw the line of best fit as accurately as you can as this will affect your answer to the other parts of the question.

ii) The graph is a straight line with an equation of the form
$\log \theta = n\log t + \log k$
$\Rightarrow \log \theta = \log t^n + \log k$
$\Rightarrow \log \theta = \log kt^n$
$\Rightarrow \quad \theta = kt^n$
The line cuts the vertical axis at 2.2 so
$\log_{10} k = 2.2$
$\Rightarrow \quad k = 10^{2.2}$
$\Rightarrow \quad k = 158.489 \ldots = 158.5\ (1\ \text{d.p.})$
The gradient of the line is

> The line passes through the points $(0, 2.2)$ and $(0.6, 1.81)$

$\dfrac{2.2 - 1.81}{0 - 0.6} = -0.65$
$\Rightarrow n = -0.65$
So the equation of the line is $\theta = 158.5t^{-0.65}$

iii) To find the temperature after 15 minutes, substitute $t = 15$ into the equation of the line.
$\theta = 158.489 \ldots \times 15^{-0.65} = 27.260 \ldots$
The temperature will be $27.3°$ after 15 minutes.

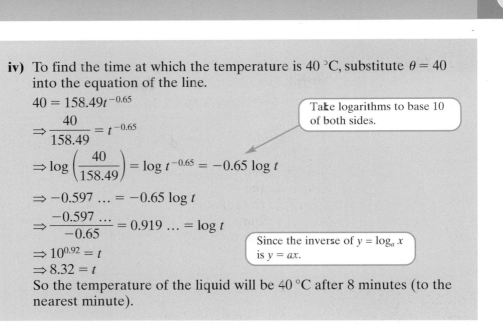

iv) To find the time at which the temperature is 40 °C, substitute $\theta = 40$ into the equation of the line.

$$40 = 158.49t^{-0.65}$$

> Take logarithms to base 10 of both sides.

$$\Rightarrow \frac{40}{158.49} = t^{-0.65}$$

$$\Rightarrow \log\left(\frac{40}{158.49}\right) = \log t^{-0.65} = -0.65 \log t$$

$$\Rightarrow -0.597 \ldots = -0.65 \log t$$

$$\Rightarrow \frac{-0.597 \ldots}{-0.65} = 0.919 \ldots = \log t$$

> Since the inverse of $y = \log_a x$ is $y = ax$.

$$\Rightarrow 10^{0.92} = t$$

$$\Rightarrow 8.32 = t$$

So the temperature of the liquid will be 40 °C after 8 minutes (to the nearest minute).

Plotting log y against x

Some types of data satisfy the relationship $y = ka^x$. In these cases plotting log y against x gives a straight line.

$$y = ka^x$$
$$\Rightarrow \log y = \log ka^x$$

> Using the laws of logarithms.

$$\Rightarrow \log y = \log a^x + \log k$$
$$\log y = x \log a + \log k$$

> This is the equation of a straight line such as $y = mx + c$ with gradient $\log_{10} a$ and intercept $\log_{10} k$.

EXAMPLE 2

The population, P, of sparrows in a region is modelled by $P = ka^t$, where t is the time in years. The table shows the population over a 5-year period.

Year (t)	1	2	3	4	5
Population (P)	390	440	495	645	794

i) Plot the graph of $\log_{10} P$ against t and use the graph to find the equation for P in terms of t.

ii) Use the equation to find the population after 8 years.

iii) After how long will the population be greater than 2000 according to this model?

SOLUTION

i)

t	1	2	3	4	5
$\mathrm{Log}_{10}\,P$	2.59	2.64	2.69	2.81	2.9

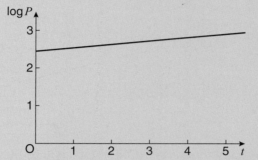

The line cuts the vertical axis at $\log_{10} k = 2.45$
so $k = 10^{2.45} \Rightarrow k = 281.8$ (1 d.p.)
The line goes through $(2, 2.64)$ and $(0, 2.45)$ so its gradient, $\log a$, is given by

$$\log_{10} a = \frac{2.64 - 2.45}{2 - 0} = \frac{0.19}{2} = 0.095$$

$$\Rightarrow \quad a = 10^{0.095} = 1.24 \text{ (2 d.p.)}$$

So the equation of the line is $P = 281.8 \times 1.24^t$

ii) To find the population after 8 years, substitute $t = 8$ into the equation
of the curve $P = 281.8 \times 1.24^8$
$P = 1575$ (nearest whole number)

iii) To find when the population will be greater than 2000, substitute
$P = 2000$ in the equation

$$281.8 \times 1.24^t = 2000$$

$$\Rightarrow 1.24^t = \frac{2000}{281.8} = 7.097 \dots$$

$$\Rightarrow t\log 1.24 = \log 7.097 \longleftarrow \boxed{\text{Take logarithms to base 10 of both sides.}}$$

$$t = \frac{\log 7.097}{\log 1.24} = 9.11$$

So the population will be greater than 2000 after 9.11 years.

LINKS

Pure Mathematics   Natural Logarithms and Exponentials (C3).

Test Yourself ⟩L

1 The graph shows the result of plotting $\log_{10} y$ against x.

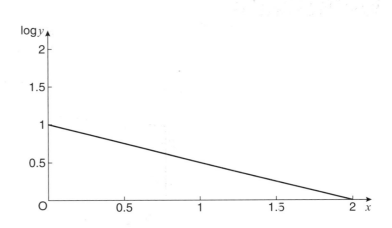

The relationship between x and y is of the form $y = k \times T^x$. Which of the following are the values of T and k, to two decimal places?

A $T = 0.32$ and $k = 10$

B $T = 0.32$ and $k = 1$

C $T = -\frac{1}{2}$ and $k = 10$

D $T = -\frac{1}{2}$ and $k = 1$

2 The relationship between a company's profits in thousands of Euros (P) and time in months (T) is found to be $P = 20T^{-0.65}$ (all numbers to 2 s.f.). Which graph represents this relationship?

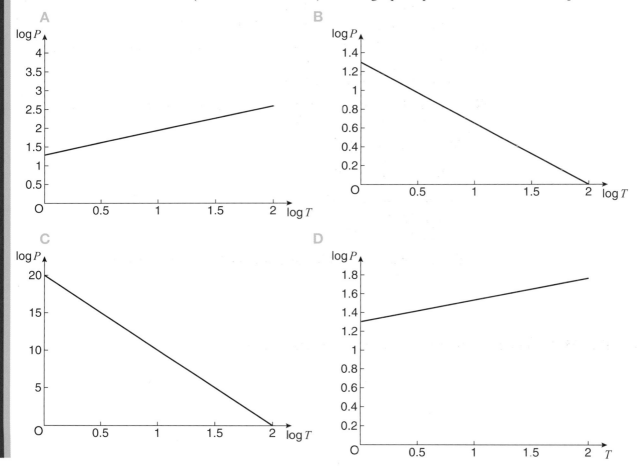

3 In an experiment, a variable, y, is measured at different times, t. The graph shows $\log_{10} y$ against $\log_{10} t$.

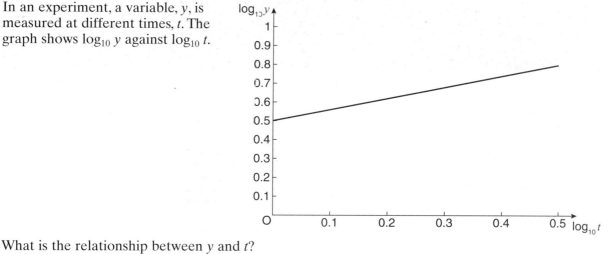

What is the relationship between y and t?

A $y = 3.16t^{1.67}$ B $y = 3.16t^{0.6}$ C $y = 0.5t^{0.6}$ D $y = 3.16t^{-0.22}$

4 The area of a patch of mould grows over time. Scientists measure the area, A cm^2, at 3-hourly intervals. The table shows the results of these measurements.

Time (hours)	3	6	9	12	15
Area (cm²)	13	19	24	28	31

What is the relationship between area and time?

A $A = 8.5 + 1.5t$ B $A = 10.5 \times 1.075^t$ C $A = \frac{1}{2} \times t^8$ D $A = 8\sqrt{t}$

Exam-Style Question ▷L

The table shows a firm's monthly profits for the first six months of the year, to the nearest £100.

Month (x)	1	2	3	4	5	6
Profit (P)	7900	8800	10 000	11 400	12 600	13 500

The firm's profits are modelled by $P = ka^x$, where a and k are constants.

i) Complete the table below and plot $\log_{10} P$ against x. Draw a line of best fit for the data.

Month (x)	1	2	3	4	5	6
Profit (P)	7900	8800	10 000	11 400	12 600	13 500
Log$_{10}$ P						

ii) Use your graph to find an equation for P in terms of x.

iii) Using this model, predict the profit for month 12 to the nearest £100.

Index

angles
  positive and negative 49
  radians 60–3
  trigonometric ratios 48, 49, 51–2, 82
arc length 60, 82
area between curve and x axis
  by integration 34–6
  trapezium rule 38, 40–1
area between two curves 38–40
area of a triangle 55, 56, 82
arithmetic progressions (A.P.s) 6–7

base of a logarithm 70–1

calculators, integration 35
chords, approximation of gradient of a curve 10
common difference, arithmetic progressions 6
common ratio, geometric progressions 6, 7–8, 73
constant of integration 30
convergent sequences 2
cosine (cos) 48–9, 50–2, 62, 82, 83
cosine curve 50, 83
cosine rule 55, 57–8
curves
  area between curve and x axis
    by integration 35–6
    trapezium rule 38, 40–1
  area between two curves 38–40
  equation of a normal 19–20
  equation of a tangent 18–20
  finding equation by integration 31–2
  gradient 10
  gradient function 11
  stationary points 22–4
  transformations 65–7

decreasing functions 26
definite integration 34–6, 83
  area between two curves 38–40
derivatives 11–12
  second derivatives 26, 27–28
differentiation 11–12, 83
  fractional powers of x 15–16
  negative powers of x 14–15
  second derivatives 26, 27–28

exponential functions 70, 73

fractional powers of x
  differentiation 15–16
  integration 44–6

geometric progressions (G.P.s) 6, 7–8, 73
gradient of a curve 10
gradient function 10, 11
  increasing and decreasing functions 26–7
graphs
  of exponential functions 73
  plotting log y against log x 75–7
  plotting log y against x 77–8
  of trigonometric functions 50, 53, 83
  see also curves

increasing functions 26–7
indefinite integration 30–2, 83
inflection, points of 22, 24
  second derivatives 26
integration
  definite 34, 83

area between curve and x axis 35–6
  area between two curves 38–40
indefinite 30–2, 83
of negative and fractional powers 44–6
use of calculators 35

limits
  convergent sequences 2
  gradient of a curve 10
local maximum and minimum points 22–4
  second derivatives 26, 28
logarithms 70–1, 82
  laws of 71–2
  plotting log y against log x 75–7
  plotting log y against x 77–8
  solving equations 72

modelling 75
  plotting log y against x 77–8
  plotting log y against log x 75–7

negative angles 49
negative areas 35, 36
negative powers of x
  differentiation 14–15
  integration 44–6
normal to a curve 19–20

oscillating sequences 1

periodic sequences 1
positive angles 49

radians 60–3, 82
reflections 65, 66

second derivatives 26, 27–8
sector, area of 60, 82
sequences 1–2, 4
  see also arithmetic progressions; geometric progressions
series 1, 3–4
  see also arithmetic progressions; geometric progressions
sine (sin) 48–9, 50–2, 62, 82
sine curve 50, 53, 83
  transformations 65–7
sine rule 55, 56–7, 82
standard results, differentiation 11–12, 14
stationary points 22–4
  second derivatives 26, 28
stretches 65, 66, 67
sum of terms of a series 3
sum to infinity, geometric progressions 6, 8

tangents to a curve
  equation of 18–20
  gradients 10
tangent (tan, trigonometric function) 48–9, 50–2, 62, 82, 83
  graph of 50, 83
terms of a sequence 1–4
transformation of curves 65–7
translations 65, 66, 67
trapezium rule 38, 40–1
triangle, area of 55, 56, 82
trigonometry 48–9, 50–2, 82
  graphs of functions 50, 53
  sine and cosine rules 55–8
  transformation of curves 65–7

unit circle 49

Formulae and results

Here are some formulae and results which you will need to recall or derive for the C2 examination. There is an underlying assumption that students already know all the results needed for GCSE Mathematics. You are also expected to recall or derive C1 results that are not given in the examination booklet. The following list is not exhaustive, and you should check with your teacher before your examination.

Logarithms and exponentials

$\log_a (xy) = \log_a x + \log_a y$ $\qquad\qquad \log_a \left(\dfrac{x}{y}\right) = \log_a x - \log_a y$

$\log_a (x^n) = n \log_a x$ $\qquad\qquad\qquad \log_a (\sqrt[n]{x}) = \dfrac{1}{n}\log_a x$

$\log_a \left(\dfrac{1}{x}\right) = -\log_a x$

$\log_a a = 1$ $\qquad\qquad\qquad\qquad\qquad \log_a 1 = 0$

$y = a^x \Leftrightarrow x = \log_a y$

Trigonometric ratios of some angles

θ	$0°$	$30°$	$45°$	$60°$	$90°$	$180°$
$\sin \theta$	0	$\dfrac{1}{2}$	$\dfrac{1}{\sqrt{2}}$	$\dfrac{\sqrt{3}}{2}$	1	0
$\cos \theta$	1	$\dfrac{\sqrt{3}}{2}$	$\dfrac{1}{\sqrt{2}}$	$\dfrac{1}{2}$	0	-1
$\tan \theta$	0	$\dfrac{1}{\sqrt{3}}$	1	$\sqrt{3}$	$-$	0

Trigonometric identities

$\dfrac{\sin \theta}{\cos \theta} = \tan \theta$ $\qquad\qquad\qquad \sin^2 \theta + \cos^2 \theta = 1$

Triangles

Area $= \frac{1}{2}ab \sin C = \frac{1}{2}bc \sin A = \frac{1}{2}ca \sin B$

Sine rule: $\dfrac{a}{\sin A} = \dfrac{b}{\sin B} = \dfrac{c}{\sin C}$

Circular measure

2π radians $= 360°$ $\qquad$ Arc length $s = r\theta$ $\qquad$ Area of sector $\frac{1}{2}r^2\theta$

Formulae and results

Trigonometric relationships

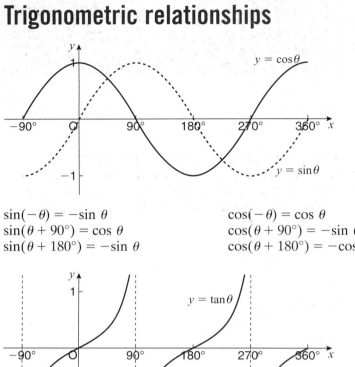

$\sin(-\theta) = -\sin\theta$

$\sin(\theta + 90°) = \cos\theta$

$\sin(\theta + 180°) = -\sin\theta$

$\cos(-\theta) = \cos\theta$

$\cos(\theta + 90°) = -\sin\theta$

$\cos(\theta + 180°) = -\cos\theta$

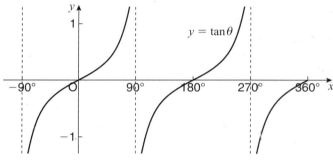

$\tan(-\theta) = -\tan\theta$

$\tan(\theta + 180°) = \tan\theta$

Differentiation

Differentiation from first principles

$$\frac{dy}{dx} = \lim_{\delta x \to 0}\frac{\delta y}{\delta x} = \lim_{\delta x \to 0}\frac{f(x + \delta x) - f(x)}{\delta x}$$

$\dfrac{dy}{dx}$ is also written as $f'(x)$

For $y = x^n$, $\dfrac{dy}{dx} = nx^{n-1}$

For $y = f(x) + g(x)$, $\dfrac{dy}{dx} = f'(x) + g'(x)$

Integration

$$\int x^n dx = \frac{x^{n-1}}{n-1} + c, n \neq -1$$

$$\int (f'(x) + g'(x))dx = f(x) + g(x) + c$$

Definite integrals

$\displaystyle\int_a^b f(x)dx$ gives the area of the region bounded by $y = f(x)$, the x-axis and the lines $x = a$ and $x = b$.

$$\int_a^b f(x)dx + \int_b^c f(x)dx = \int_a^c f(x)dx$$

$$\int_b^a f(x)dx = -\int_a^b f(x)dx$$